Contents

KT-131-133

WARRINGTON HOSPITAL LIBRARY

4339501003098442772b012

Acknowledgements

Every effort has been made to contact copyright holders of material reproduced in this book. Any omissions will be rectified in subsequent printings if notice is given to the publishers.

The authors and publishers would like to thank the following for permission to reproduce photographs.

Alamy: page 156
John Birdsall Photography: pages 16, 133
Harcourt Education Ltd/Gareth Boden: pages 2, 20, 30, 41, 52, 77, 94, 96, 129, 138, 160, 170, 173
Mary Evans Picture Library: page 95
Robert Harding Picture Library: page 192
Photodisc: page 86
Science Photo Library: page 128

The authors and publishers would like to thank the City and Guilds of London Institute for permission to reproduce sample test questions and glossary. City & Guilds accepts no liability for the contents of this book.

Introduction

Choosing a career in care means that you have opted for one of the most rewarding jobs. You will have the opportunity to enable, empower and support those who use social care and health services. The fact that you have reached the stage of working towards a qualification shows that you have the first, all-important building blocks to develop a successful career in care. The best care professionals realise that caring is about much more than just being a 'kind person' or someone who 'likes people' – those factors are important, but they need to be backed up with a great deal of knowledge and understanding, and a wide range of skills.

As you progress through your Certificate in Supporting Care Practice, you will be developing an understanding of the rights, needs and hopes of the service users you work with. You will also learn about the important skills you need in order to work effectively in care. The Technical Certificate forms part of the Modern Apprenticeship programme in care, so you are likely to be studying this qualification alongside the assessment of your NVQ. This provides you with an excellent chance to learn at the same time as gaining practical skills, and you should have every opportunity to put your knowledge into practice.

The book is designed to match the units in your qualification. Each of the units has several outcomes. These show what you will know by the time you have finished learning all the information in the unit. For example, in Unit 1, when you have completed all the learning in the first outcome, you will be able to:

▶ relate to others in an anti-discriminatory way.

The sections in this book covering each outcome contain all the knowledge you will need to complete the outcomes. Throughout the book you will find ideas on how your knowledge can be applied in your own workplace, in the form of 'Check it out' activities. Take the time to work through each of these, because you will be surprised at how much more you remember about ideas and knowledge you have tried out in practice.

There are also Case Studies throughout the book, which will provide you with the chance to think about, and discuss with others, some of the situations you may be faced with in doing your job.

At the end of each outcome, you will find an activity that is designed to help you provide evidence for your Key Skills award. The activities are relevant to the outcomes and will help you to think about what you have learned. On page 196 there is a table showing where opportunities for demonstrating Key Skills are provided in these activities.

You will need to complete an assignment set by City and Guilds in order to show that you have successfully achieved the requirements of each unit. There is also a written test which covers knowledge from all of the units in the qualification. Here are some examples of the types of questions you can expect in this test.

---

1 a) Give one example of discrimination.
    b) Identify TWO examples of anti-discriminatory legislation.
    c) Describe how legislation can protect vulnerable people from discrimination.
    d) Explain how the care worker can help promote individuals' rights.

2 a) Give TWO examples of unacceptable behaviour.
    b) Suggest reasons why this behaviour may occur.
    c) Explain ways of preventing challenging behaviour.

3 a) Describe THREE different types of abuse.
    b) Describe the signs that may indicate that someone is being abused in these ways.

4 a) Explain the precautions to be taken in order to maintain confidentiality when receiving, passing on or storing information.
    b) Evaluate the importance of maintaining confidentiality in the Care sector.

Sample test questions are available from City and Guilds. It is a good idea to practise writing some answers, so that you gain confidence.

On page 194, the Glossary of Terms produced by City and Guilds for this qualification is reproduced. Make sure you understand all these terms before you take your test.

I hope that what you learn from this book will help you to enjoy the work you carry out, and that you will continue to expand and develop your own knowledge and skills throughout your career.

Good luck with your course
Yvonne Nolan

Promoting diversity

This is the essential unit which will underpin all the work you do in a care setting. Regardless of the task you are undertaking, or the service user you are working with, everything you do must be carried out in accordance with the principles you will learn here. By the time you have successfully completed this unit you will know about service users' rights and about the important differences between the values and beliefs of individuals, and how these differences contribute to the overall quality and richness of local and national communities. You will know how you can make sure that you recognise and respect difference in the way you practise.

This unit will give you the opportunity to look at your own performance in a care setting and help you to practise in a way which is anti-discriminatory and anti-oppressive. This unit will also help you to understand how to respond when faced with an abusive situation or with challenging behaviour.

Outcome 1: Relate to others in an anti-discriminatory way

The rights your service users have

Rights and responsibilities are a huge subject. In order to look at rights in terms of how they affect the people you work with and provide care for, it is helpful to discuss them under the following headings:

▶ basic human rights
▶ rights under charters, guidelines and policies
▶ rights provided by law.

What are responsibilities? They are the other side of the coin to rights – most of our responsibilities are about protecting, improving or not infringing other people's rights. Responsibilities are the balance for rights, and it is impossible to consider one without the other.

Basic human rights

In 1949 the United Nations Universal Declaration of Human Rights identified a set of basic rights which everyone should have. The Declaration sets out to promote and encourage acceptance of personal, civil, political, economic, social and cultural rights, which are only limited by the need to respect the rights and freedoms of others and the needs of morality, public order and general welfare.

Everyone has personal rights, but they must be balanced with responsibilities to others.

For many people throughout the world, these are rights they can only hope for, and not rights they currently enjoy. The United Nations has a Commission on Human Rights which works to promote the world-wide acceptance of these basic rights and to identify abuses and violations of human rights throughout the world.

Personal basic rights

Alongside the basic rights conferred by charters and laws, there are also personal rights which apply to all of us. For example, someone may say 'I've got a right to be angry, haven't I?' Of course everyone has a right to be angry, or to be upset or frustrated when things go wrong, or to feel vulnerable and afraid in new or threatening situations. Everyone has a right to feel and express basic human emotions, but the responsibility that goes alongside this is that you cannot express them in a way which oppresses or harms someone else.

This is not always an easy area for workers in care settings to manage. A service user who is angry about or frustrated by his or her condition may express some of the anger by being rude or aggressive to other service users. Clearly, this cannot be allowed to happen, because there is always an important balance to be achieved between the rights of the service user and the rights of others.

There are balances in the exercise of other personal rights, such as the right to make mistakes or to get things wrong. Of course everyone is entitled to try out new ideas and to explore and develop as an individual. This inevitably will lead to mistakes and errors. Most of the time this is acknowledged as an essential part of the learning process. As the saying goes, 'the person who never made a mistake never made anything'. However, as always, there are balances to be found. Some people have less room to make mistakes than others:

▶ an air traffic controller who makes a mistake could be the cause of a major catastrophe
▶ a lorry, bus or train driver who makes a mistake could cause disaster on a large scale
▶ a health professional who prescribes or administers the wrong medication could cause major damage.

In general, everyone should be able to make mistakes without being ridiculed or humiliated. But there will always be some exceptional circumstances where mistakes cannot be tolerated.

Check it out

In pairs, make notes about at least three things you have learned by making mistakes or getting things wrong. Your examples may be at work, or around the house, or when learning new skills such as driving or a new sport, or even from school. Tell each other about what you learned and how you have been able to use this to your benefit.

Rights under charters, guidelines and policies

These are rights which do not have the force of law, but which are designed to improve the services people receive.

The document called 'Your Guide to the NHS', published in 2000, sets out what people can expect from the National Health Service. It covers issues such as people's rights to receive care from a GP, how long they can reasonably be expected to wait for a hospital appointment, and how long before urgent and non-urgent treatment. However, it is different from the Patient's Charter which it replaced because it also identifies the responsibilities of patients (see page 18). The guide includes information on how patients can use services and how they can complain if necessary.

Even though this is set out as only a guidance document, the government has made it clear that this is the way in which the Health Service is expected to operate. This means that the performance of all NHS trusts is measured against this guidance.

Charters exist for other services, such as the Passenger's Charter, which lays down standards which can be expected for rail travel.

The key role of charters is to make the expected standards public, so there can be no argument that service users are being unreasonable in their demands, or their expectations are too high. If people know what they have a right to expect, then they can take steps to complain and have things put right if the standards are not met.

Check it out

The organisation you work for is likely to have policies and statements about how it works. Find out what they are, and see how you feel your workplace measures up to its stated aims, mission statements and public charters.

Rights provided by law

The Human Rights Act received the royal assent on 9 November 1998 and the majority of its provisions came into force on 2 October 2000. The Human Rights Act means that residents of the United Kingdom – this Act applies in England, Scotland, Wales and Northern Ireland – will now be entitled to seek help from the courts if they believe that their human rights have been infringed.

Organisations subject to the Human Rights Act 1998

Residential homes or nursing homes	These perform functions which would otherwise be performed by a local authority
Charities	
Voluntary organisations	
Public service	This could include the privatised utilities, such as gas, electric and water companies

It is likely that anyone who works in health or care will be working within the provisions of the Human Rights Act, which guarantees the following rights.

1 **The right to life.** Public authorities must not cause the death of any person and they have a positive duty to protect life.
2 **The right to freedom from torture and inhuman or degrading treatment or punishment.** This ill-treatment relates to both mental and physical suffering. One of the factors which is taken into account under this right is the severity and duration of the torture, inhuman or degrading treatment and the vulnerability of the victim.
3 **The right to freedom from slavery, servitude and forced or compulsory labour.** Slavery means that a person is owned by somebody else like a piece of property. Servitude is defined as a person not being owned by someone else but being forced to provide service for them and unable to leave.
4 **The right to liberty and security of person.** People have a right not to be arrested or detained except when the detention is authorised by law.
5 **The right to a fair and a public trial within a reasonable time.** This right covers all criminal and most civil cases as well as tribunals and some internal hearings.
6 **The right to freedom from retrospective criminal law and no punishment without law.** This right means that people cannot be convicted for an act which was not a criminal offence at the time it was committed, nor can they face a punishment which was not in force when the act happened.
7 **The right to respect for private and family life, home and correspondence.** This is one of the very far-reaching parts of the Human Rights Act. Public authorities may only interfere in someone's private life when they have the legal authority to do so.

8 **The right to freedom of thought, conscience and religion.** Under this right people can hold whatever thoughts, positions of conscience or religious beliefs they wish.

9 **The right to freedom of expression.** Freedom of expression includes what is said in conversation or speeches, what is published in books, articles or leaflets, what is broadcast and what is presented as art or placed on the Internet. In fact, any means of communication.

10 **The right to freedom of assembly and association.** This includes the right of people to demonstrate peacefully and to join or choose not to join trade unions.

11 **The right to marry and found a family.** This part of the Act is particularly relevant to rules and policies concerning adoption and fostering.

12 **The prohibition of discrimination in the enjoyment of convention rights.** The Act recognises that not all differences in treatment are discriminatory; those that are discriminating are defined as those which have no objective or reasonable justification.

13 **The right to peaceful enjoyment of possessions and protection of property.** The Act defines many possessions as property; not just houses or cars, but things like shares, licences and goodwill.

14 **The right of access to an education.** The right of access to education must be balanced against the resources available. This right may be relevant to the exclusion of disruptive pupils from schools, and may also prove to be very relevant for children with special needs.

15 **The right of free elections.** They must be free and fair and be held at reasonable intervals. Access issues are also involved, such as making sure that people with disabilities or those who are ill are still able to participate.

16 **The right not to be subjected to the death penalty.** This provision abolishes the death penalty.

Law, rights and discrimination

Discrimination is a denial of rights. Discrimination can be based on race, gender, disability or sexual orientation. The main Acts of Parliament which are to do with rights are:

▶ the Race Relations Act 1976
▶ the Equal Pay Act 1970
▶ the Sex Discrimination Act 1975
▶ the Disability Discrimination Act 1995.

Race Relations Act 1976

This Act prohibits all forms of racial discrimination, whether in employment, housing or services. It also makes it an offence to incite (encourage) racial hatred. The Act covers all discrimination whether it is about colour, nationality or race, and forbids both direct and indirect discrimination.

Direct discrimination occurs when people are prevented from doing something because of their race as, for example, in the two adverts shown on the next page.

> English workers wanted
> for new factory
> Good wages

> Flat to let
> Two bedrooms
> No Irish applicants please

Both of those adverts are blatantly racist and would not be seen anywhere today, but 50 years ago such adverts were commonplace.

Indirect discrimination is more subtle. This can work by imposing conditions which some people would find impossible to meet, as in the advert below, for example.

> **Bricklayer required**
> **Must speak fluent**
> **English**

This is indirect discrimination because it may exclude people who are fairly recent immigrants. There can be no justification for this requirement if the work does not require use of language or contact with the public.

Another example might be a sheltered housing scheme which has a rule about tenants not being allowed to cook highly spiced food because of the smell. It would be breaking the law, because Asian food tends to be highly spiced whereas English food does not. This would discriminate against Asian tenants being able to cook their native food.

People's rights to housing and provision of services are also supported by the Act.

Sounds great …

but – *the rights can be difficult to enforce. Support is given to people bringing cases under the Act by the Commission for Racial Equality, but proving discrimination is notoriously difficult.*

DID YOU KNOW?

Women comprise 50 per cent of the world population, do 90 per cent of the world's work, earn 10 per cent of the world's income and own 1 per cent of the world's wealth. (UNESCO)

The Race Relations Act requires that there be no racial discrimination, either direct or indirect, in employment matters. However, employment figures for black and Asian people prove that the Act has not achieved its objective.

For example, figures from the Lord Chancellor's department show that there are no black Law Lords or Appeal Court judges, and only seven black Circuit Court judges out of a total of 614. People from ethnic minorities occupy only three positions as District Judges in magistrates' courts, out of 103.

A similar picture is presented by employment patterns in the police force. Despite a wide-ranging and highly publicised examination of racism and its consequences within the police, there has been little increase in employment of black and Asian people as police officers. Between 1995 and 2001 the percentage of police officers from racial minorities increased only from 1.75 per cent to 2.3 per cent across England and Wales. This represents an increase from 2,223 officers in 1995 to 2,975 in 2001.

There has been a small increase in the numbers of black and Asian police officers achieving promotion, but the percentage remains tiny.

Recently there have been several highly publicised cases where black or Asian members of the armed forces have received compensation after being the victims of racial abuse within the armed forces. Historically, there has been a problem with under-representation of ethnic minorities in the armed forces. The figures for 1994 showed that in all three of the armed services, black and ethnic minority service personnel represented on average only about 1.3 per cent of the total. Only 13 per cent of black applicants were accepted by the Army, whereas approximately 25 per cent of white applicants were accepted.

Forces	% black & ethnic recruits
Royal Navy	1.1%
Army	1.5%
Royal Air Force	1.4%

These figures make it clear that legislation alone is not sufficient to ensure that people are not discriminated against and are able to exercise their rights. Legislation will not be effective unless attitudes change, and any change in attitude requires a long period of education, both formal and informal.

Many employers and a wide range of organisations claim to be non-racist and to have a policy of equal opportunities. However, the old saying: 'I cannot hear what you are saying – the things you do are speaking too loudly', is appropriate for a great many organisations in the UK today.

Check it out

Find out the percentage of your local population who are from black, Asian or other ethnic minority backgrounds. Compare this to the numbers of people employed in your organisation. Check whether the overall work force reflects the make-up of your local population, then check the number of people in senior management positions in your organisation. How many of them are from black, Asian or other ethnic minority backgrounds? How does this compare with the make-up of the overall work force?

Equal Pay Act 1970

The Equal Pay Act 1970 (amended 1983) is designed to make discrimination on the grounds of gender illegal. It provides a woman with the right to be employed on the same terms and conditions as a man doing an equivalent job, or work of equal value. For example, it has been judged in a court of law that a female canteen cook's work is of equal value to that of a male joiner, painter or sanitation engineer.

This type of legislation is common in many countries now, so the situation for women's pay has improved.

Sounds great …

but – *it is often the kind of work which women do, much of it part-time or low-paid, which causes the difference in average pay*

but – *of course, the work which women do at home is unpaid!*

The 'pay gap' – the difference between average male full-time earnings and those of women – is 18 per cent. In other words, women earn on average 82 per cent of the wages men earn.

DID YOU KNOW?

Average male income in the UK is twice that of women. This takes into account income from all sources, so it is not just about wages, but benefits, pensions and self-employed earnings.

Source: *Women and Equality Unit, DTI*

Sex Discrimination Act 1975

This Act is designed to provide equal rights to men and women in respect of employment, goods, services and facilities. It prevents discrimination either directly or indirectly which would prevent women from being employed or receiving a service in the same way as men. The Equal Opportunities

Commission supports the working of the law by supporting cases, investigating abuses and promoting equality.

Women who, for example, have been repeatedly passed over for promotion at work, even though men who are less qualified have achieved success, can use the Sex Discrimination Act. There have been several well-publicised cases in public services such as the police and fire services.

Women have a right to be admitted to all public places on the same basis as men. This means that there are no longer any 'men only' bars – unless they are in private clubs, such as golf clubs.

Men can also use the Act if they have been unfairly discriminated against. For example, the fact that most baby-changing facilities are located in women's public lavatories means that a man who has the care of a baby will have difficulty finding a suitable place to change the baby.

The Act deals with both direct and indirect discrimination. For example, a woman could take an employer to court if a job was advertised like the one below.

Care assistants needed for residential home

Must be experienced. Applicants should be at least 5 ft 10 in tall.

Height is not a reasonable requirement in order to do the job. Far more women are below 5ft 10in than men, so the advert discriminates against women.

It would also be discriminatory against men if it advertised for people under 5ft 4in!

In the provision of services, if, for instance, a primary care team decided no longer to provide treatment for people with osteoporosis, a challenge could be made on the grounds that it is primarily women who suffer from the condition and therefore the decision would discriminate unfairly against women. Similarly, if the group decided not to treat people with prostate problems, the decision could be open to challenge by men.

Sounds great …

but – *like racial discrimination, sex discrimination is difficult to prove.*

Women tend to work in low-paid occupations such as clerical, catering, hairdressing, caring and other service industries. The 'glass ceiling' is a term used for the barriers which prevent women achieving promotion to senior positions. Many of these barriers are not obvious but are composed of factors such as working arrangements and working hours, the problems of balancing work and family, difficulties in mobility and the outdated attitude of some male senior managers.

Women in management

- ▶ Women comprise 30 per cent of managers in England, 29 per cent in Scotland and 33 per cent in Wales.
- ▶ While women make up 73 per cent of managers in health and social services, they make up only 6 per cent in production.
- ▶ Women's representation also varies by sector. While 40 per cent of managers in the public sector are female, in the private sector it is just 28 per cent.
- ▶ Data from the National Management Salary Survey in 2001 revealed that the average female manager earned £34,789, while the average male manager earned £40,289. Women managers therefore earned around 86 per cent of the average managerial salary for men.

Women in the boardroom

In all UK listed companies:

- ▶ less than 1 per cent of chairpersons are women
- ▶ 4 per cent of executive director posts (including chief executive officer) are held by women
- ▶ 6 per cent of non-executive director posts (employed largely to offer strategic, specific and objective advice at board meetings) are held by women
- ▶ overall, 4 per cent of directorships are held by women.

In FTSE 100 companies:

- ▶ just over one in ten non-executive posts and one in 40 executive posts are held by women
- ▶ only one company had a female chief executive officer in 2002
- ▶ only 7.2 per cent of directorships are held by women and 39 firms have no female directors.

Within the legal and judicial system women, like black and Asian people, are under-represented. Only 7 per cent of High Court judges and 15 per cent of recorders are women. There are no women Law Lords and only one female Appeal Court judge. Among police officers 16 per cent are women but only 3 per cent of Chief Constables are female; in the armed forces there are only two women at the rank of Brigadier or Commodore and none above this rank. Even within the academic world, women are not equally represented: at Oxford and Cambridge women represent an average of only 16 per cent of lecturers and 6.5 per cent of professors.

Just by providing women with rights in respect of employment the Sex Discrimination Act will not necessarily change attitudes. This is a long and slow process, and even over the almost 30 years that this Act has been in place, progress has been painfully slow.

CASE STUDY

The A family live in the Midlands. Mr A is from Pakistan, and he is very devout in his Muslim beliefs. The tradition in the area he comes from is that all young men and women are expected to have their marriages arranged by their families. Mr A's daughter M is 16 years old, she was born in the UK, speaks with a local accent, and has friends, both Muslim and non-Muslim in the area. However, her father has now decided that it is time that she was married. He has arranged for her to be married to a distant relative from the family's home town in Pakistan. M is not happy at the prospect, and wants to meet someone in the UK. She is reluctant to go to Pakistan, where she has never been before.

1 What are Mr A's rights? What are his responsibilities?
2 What are M's rights?
3 Does M have responsibilities?
4 What decisions could be made?
5 Do any laws affect this situation?

Disability Discrimination Act 1995

This Act is designed to provide new rights for people with disabilities, in:

- employment
- access to education and transport
- housing
- obtaining goods and services.

The Act defines disability as a condition which makes it difficult for someone to carry out normal day-to-day activities. The disability can be physical, sensory (affecting the senses) or mental but, to be covered by the Act, it must be substantial and have a long-term effect. This means that the disability must last, or be expected to last, for at least 12 months.

Under the Act employers must not treat a disabled person less favourably than an able-bodied person. An employer must examine the changes that need to be made to the workplace, or to how the work is carried out, in order to make it possible for someone with a disability to do the job.

Access rights to education and transport for people with disabilities means that schools and colleges will have to produce details of how any student will be able to access courses, regardless of disability. All new taxis, buses, trains and coaches have to be accessible for disabled people.

Landlords are not allowed to discriminate against anyone with a disability when letting a property, or to charge a higher rent than they would for a non-disabled person.

Shops, restaurants and anyone who provides a service have to ensure that disabled people are able to make use of the service and are not charged more

than a non-disabled person. They have to make it easier for disabled people to use their services by providing any adaptations needed or by arranging for other ways of using the service, for example, by providing a mail order catalogue.

Sounds great ...

but – *most of the provisions are only enforced 'if it is reasonable to do so'*

but – *one of the considerations which people can take into account when considering if it is 'reasonable' to change things for disabled people is the cost – so, if it would cost too much to put in a ramp, the shop can justify not doing so.*

DID YOU KNOW?

There are over 6.5 million disabled people in the UK – and 31 per cent of these are currently employed.

Only 17 per cent of disabled people were born with their disability.

REMEMBER

▶ Acts of Parliament don't change attitudes.

▶ Discrimination may be unlawful, but people still have the right to think, write and speak as they wish.

Stereotypes

One of the main reasons why discrimination happens is that so much fear and misunderstanding of others is spread through stereotyping. Prejudice is what makes people think in stereotypes and, equally, stereotypes support prejudice. Stereotypes are an easy way of thinking about the world. They suggest that all people over 65 are frail and walk with a stick, that all black young people who live in inner cities are on drugs, that all overweight people are lazy, or that all families have a mother, father and two children. These stereotypes, or ways of looking at the world, are often reinforced by the media or by advertising. Television programmes will often portray violent, criminal characters as young and black.

Next time you watch television, note down the number of adverts for cars which show trendy, good-looking young business people with a wealthy lifestyle. The advertisers attempt to convince us that buying that particular brand of car will make us good-looking and trendy and give us the kind of lifestyle portrayed.

1 How many people do you know with those particular makes of car who are anything like the people in the adverts?

2 How many do you know who wish they were?

What effect do stereotypes have?

The effect of stereotypes is to make us jump to conclusions about people. How many times have you felt uneasy seeing a young man with a shaved head walking towards you? You know nothing about him, but the way he looks has made you form an opinion about him. If you have a picture in your mind of a social worker or a police officer, think about how much that is influenced by the media – do they really all look like that?

1 What do you think each of these people does for a living?

2 What kind of place does each of them live in?

3 Why have you given the answers you have?

Accents can often evoke prejudice. Try to be aware of what regional accents mean – think about these stereotypes:

People from ...	are known as ...	are thought to be ...
Liverpool	Scousers	work-shy, scroungers, funny
Birmingham	Brummies	slow, not very bright, boring
London	Cockneys	wheeler dealers, not trustworthy, clever
Glasgow	Glaswegians	aggressive, looking for a fight, drinkers
Newcastle	Geordies	warm, friendly, tough, 'salt of the earth'

The next time you find yourself making a judgement about somebody's character based on an accent, stop and think. Try to avoid a stereotype.

'Have you heard the one about ...?'

Telling jokes at the expense of particular groups of people is similarly displaying prejudices. Stereotypes about people being mean or stupid because of their nationality fail to treat people as individuals and fail to recognise that there are individuals everywhere and that all people are different.

Check it out

Stop yourself every time you make a generalisation and look at the prejudice. Think about why you think the way you do, and do something about it. The next time you hear yourself saying 'Social workers never understand what is really needed', 'GPs always take ages to visit' or 'Our residents wouldn't be interested in that', stop and think what you are really doing.

It is probably quite correct that some social workers won't understand, maybe even all those you have met so far! But that does not necessarily apply to them all.

Perhaps most of your residents would not be interested in whatever was being suggested – a trip to the art gallery? a bike ride? or a naughty underwear party? – you cannot make that assumption. You need to ask.

Particular laws for particular people

Apart from the laws which provide rights for everyone, there are other laws which are likely to affect the particular group of individuals you work with. These laws are not only about providing people with rights, they can also be about restricting rights, when it is in someone's interests to do so.

Mental Health Act 1983

This Act affects people with mental health problems or a learning disability. People can be compulsorily sent to hospital when they are considered to be ill, or to prison if they have committed criminal offences. This is a severe restriction on people's liberty and they have rights to appeal against such detentions. Appeals are heard by special tribunals, and it is easy to see the dilemma which could exist between the rights of an individual and responsibility towards the community.

CASE STUDY

K was convicted 10 years ago of sexually abusing two children. He was diagnosed as suffering from a mental illness, and so was committed to a secure hospital under the Mental Health Act rather than being sent to prison. This type of sentence does not carry a particular length of time, but is referred to as HMP (at Her Majesty's pleasure). This means that the person will remain in a special hospital until enough evidence is put before a tribunal for a decision to be made that he or she no longer represents a risk.

K is now in his late fifties and all the psychiatric specialists are of the opinion that his illness is now 'burnt out' and he does not represent a threat to the community. His future is about to be considered by a tribunal who have the power to allow him to be released. K is a pleasant man, who is very slow in his responses. He is not at all aggressive and is very eager to please. He will do exactly as instructed, and has spent the past three years helping in the hospital kitchens. He cannot cope with complicated tasks, but can do simple jobs which do not involve much memory.

However, the local community where he lived and assaulted the children has heard about the possibility of release. There is a great deal of concern, and a local campaign has begun which claims that the tribunal has a responsibility to consider the safety of the local community. There have been threats that K will be the subject of a vigilante campaign if he is released, and the implication is that he may be harmed or forced to leave the area.

1　Whose rights should be considered in this situation?
2　Is there a responsibility for the tribunal and the psychiatrists to consider the community?
3　Whose rights are most important?
4　How could this be resolved?

Children Act 1989

This Act provides children with the right to be protected from 'significant harm'. The definition of significant harm is decided by the courts at the request of social services departments. The harm could be being inflicted by parents, or by the children themselves if they are 'beyond control' and involved in crime, drugs or prostitution.

This is also the first Act which identifies 'parental responsibility' rather than 'parental rights'. So, for the first time, children are not treated as property over which 'rights' can be exercised.

This Act also ensures that nurseries and residential schools have to reach certain standards, and that they are regularly inspected.

It gives rights to children who have been looked after by social services departments to be supported, to be assisted to become independent, and to have access to information about their lives and their own histories.

CASE STUDY

C is 15 years old. She is at a police station refusing to return home. She says that she does not get on with her parents because they are too strict and do not give her any freedom. C wants to be able to go to clubs and go out with boys, which her parents will not allow. She says that she would rather live in a children's home because there she will be allowed more freedom. She is friendly with K, a girl at her school who lives in a small children's home. C feels that K goes out and has boyfriends and can do more or less what she likes. She says that if the police or social workers send her home to her parents, then she will run away. Her parents want her to return home, and her father has arrived at the police station insisting that he is taking her home.

1 What rights does C have?
2 What rights do her parents have?
3 Do social services have any responsibility for C's safety?
4 How can this be resolved?

NHS and Community Care Act 1990

This Act gives older and disabled people rights in respect of the services they should be provided with by their social services department.

All social services departments have to publish plans about how they will run their services. These plans must include the criteria which will be used to define how services will be provided for particular needs. Everyone has a right to see the plans, and to be consulted if they belong to a group which represents people who are likely to use the services.

All people who are in need of community care have the legal right to have their needs assessed and to have services provided.

All people who are in need of community care have the right to have their needs assessed and to have services provided in accordance with the published standards. People also have a right to complain if the service is not provided.

This is a wide-ranging Act which has provided disabled and older people with more rights than they previously enjoyed, although many social services departments are struggling to provide the services with a limited amount of funding.

CASE STUDY

Mrs B is 93 years old. She cannot get out of bed, has a heart condition, emphysema and severe arthritis and requires round-the-clock care. She is unable to care for herself at all; she is unable to get out of bed without help and is extremely frail. If she were left alone she would be in grave danger of falling or she might need help with using her oxygen supply. Mrs B is not in the slightest bit confused and is very clear that she does not wish to leave her home and go into residential or nursing home care. The local NHS trust will not keep her in hospital as she does not have any acute medical needs that cannot be met in the community.

Her needs assessment has defined that she needs 24-hour care. This is presently provided by a team of carers who work for a local private care agency. The cost is several times more than the cost of providing the equivalent care in a residential setting. The local social services department is presently having to refuse services to some people because of a shortage of cash. This has been explained to Mrs B in an attempt to persuade her to agree to residential care, but she continues to insist that she wants to remain in her own home.

1 Does Mrs B have the right to insist on staying at home?
2 What are the responsibilities of social services to Mrs B? And to others in need?
3 Should Mrs B's rights be more important than the responsibilities to the rest of the community?

How to balance rights and responsibilities

It is often difficult for people to exercise their rights while ensuring that others' rights are respected. A person may have the right to live as he or she wishes, but what about the rest of the community?

CASE STUDY

G is 53 years old. She has lived alone in a large house since her mother died 10 years ago. She behaves in a strange way, often walking along the road and talking to herself. She does not acknowledge any of the neighbours, apart from shouting at local children if they venture into her very overgrown garden. She appears very dirty and dresses in the same clothes for months on end. G seems to collect old newspapers and her house is crammed with rubbish. She has 18 cats, five dogs, several ducks, 10 chickens and a goat. All the animals are well fed and cared for, but they create a considerable amount of noise and smell.

G has been assessed by a psychiatrist and is not mentally ill. The people in the local community want her to leave. They say that she causes problems with the animals, that the house is a health hazard, she frightens the children and her house is so dilapidated it makes the whole road look scruffy.

1 What rights does G have?
2 What rights do the rest of the community have?
3 Does G have any responsibility to the community she lives in?
4 Do they have any responsibility towards her?
5 How could this be resolved?

Responsibilities

'Responsibility' is a word which has meanings at many levels – it is often used to refer to the duties people take on as they grow up: buying a house, getting married, having children. All of these things bring responsibilities, but it could be argued that these responsibilities conflict with rights.

For example, looking after children is a great responsibility. It also means that people no longer have the right to please themselves about going out, or spending money as they please, because their responsibilities towards their children come before their rights to satisfy their own desires. Most people accept this willingly and take delight in providing care for their children, but some situations are not so clear cut.

Check it out

Does a person's responsibility to care for an elderly parent outweigh his or her rights to earn a living and have a social life? Discuss this with your colleagues.

The National Health Service clearly identifies the responsibilities of patients. While people have a right to expect a certain level of service from the NHS, it is clear that the health of the nation is a two-way partnership and that everyone has a responsibility to contribute. Patient responsibilities were identified in 'Your Guide to the NHS' (2000) as the following.

▶ Do what you can to look after your own health, and follow advice on a healthy lifestyle.
▶ Care for yourself when appropriate. (For example, you can treat yourself at home for common ailments such as coughs, colds and sore throats.)
▶ Give blood if you are able, and carry an organ donor card or special needs card or bracelet.
▶ Keep your appointment or let the GP, dentist, clinic or hospital know as soon as possible if you cannot make it. Book routine appointments in plenty of time.
▶ Listen carefully to advice on your treatment and medication. Tell the doctor about any treatments you are already taking.
▶ Return any equipment that is no longer needed.
▶ Pay NHS prescription charges and any other charges promptly when they are due and claim financial benefits or exemptions from these charges correctly. Treat NHS staff, fellow patients, carers and visitors politely, and with respect. Violence and racial, sexual or verbal harassment are unacceptable.

The dilemma of balancing rights and responsibilities is one most people working in care deal with on a daily basis. Think about your right to go home! There is a set time at which you should finish your shift or your day, but there are many occasions when it is not that simple. An emergency may have arisen, perhaps someone has fallen, or there may have been a death, or someone has just started to talk to you for the first time. You could be dealing with a relative who is very distressed. Any of these situations, and many more, can mean that you balance your right to finish work on time against the responsibilities you hold towards the individual needing your help, and his or her right to be helped.

Constraints and conflicts

Most care settings, whether residential or providing day-care services, involve living, sharing and working with others. Any situation which involves close and prolonged contact with others has the potential to be difficult. You only have to think about the day-to-day conflicts and difficulties which arise in most families to realise the issues involved when human beings get together in a group.

Disagreements between service users, particularly in residential or day-care settings, are not unusual and you may well find yourself being called on to act as referee. The conflicts can range from disputes over particular chairs or TV channels, to political disagreements or complaints about the behaviour of others. Conflict resolution is not an easy task, wherever you are and however large or small a scale you are working on. However, there are some basic guidelines to follow:

▶ remain calm and speak in a firm, quiet voice – do not raise your voice
▶ make it clear that physical violence is completely unacceptable
▶ make it clear that verbal abuse will not be tolerated
▶ listen in turn to both sides of the argument – don't let people interrupt each other
▶ look for reasonable compromises which involve both parties in winning some points and losing others
▶ make it clear to both sides that they will have to compromise – that total victory for one or the other is not an option.

A wide range of difficulties can arise. They can be about behaviour which is unacceptable and causes distress to others, such as playing loud music or shouting. They can also be about matters which seem trivial but can cause major irritation when people live together, such as the way someone eats, or the fact that they mutter out loud as they read the newspaper.

Sometimes conflicts can arise about behaviour which is not anyone's fault, but is the result of someone's illness or condition. For instance, sometimes people experiencing some forms of dementia may shout and moan loudly, which may be distressing and annoying to others. Some people may eat messily or dribble as the result of a physical condition, which may be unpleasant and upsetting for those who share a table with them. These situations require a great deal of tact and explanation. It is simply not possible for the individuals concerned to stop their behaviour, so those around them have to be helped to understand the reasons and to cope with the consequences.

Think about the type of arguments and disagreements which may arise in your work setting. If you have been involved in helping to resolve any such problem, make a note of what you did and how effective it was. If another member of staff was involved, note down the actions he or she took and if they were effective. See if you can work out why some actions were effective. If they were not, see if you can work out why they failed.

Working with colleagues

In any care setting, it is not only the service users who have to be together for long periods of time – the staff have to learn to work together too. This may be

the first time you have worked in a team with colleagues, or you may have moved to a new team which will function differently from the last place you worked. Each team is different!

Teams take time to learn to work together well. They go through various stages as they settle down, and every time a new team member arrives, things change. Not everyone will share the same views about how tasks should be undertaken and about the right course of action on every occasion. Much will depend on how well the team is managed. However, there are some ground rules that can be applied in most situations.

Teams have to learn to get along and work well together.

▶ Find out the ways in which decisions are reached and the team members who should be included.
▶ Always ask for advice and clarify anything you are not sure about.
▶ Do not assume that everything is the same in every workplace.
▶ Recognise that every team member, regardless of his or her role and status, has an essential contribution to make.
▶ Value the input of all colleagues and recognise its importance.
▶ Make sure that the way you work is not increasing the workload of others or hindering them in carrying out their work.

Most workplaces have a means of decision making. There could be planning and review meetings where decisions are made about service provision. Staff meetings may be the forum for making decisions about general practice matters, or there may be specific staff development and training meetings for sharing best practice. Organised meetings run by a line manager or supervisor are the best place for discussing differences about practice or decisions about a particular service user; here everyone has the chance to have a say and to take account of a range of views from other team members. A well-run staff group should also be able to reach agreement on the best course of action and make sure that all the relevant views are taken into account.

Take an example where there is a disagreement between staff members about the extent to which a service user is able to undertake his or her own care. One member of staff may see that it is important to protect the service user from risk, while another feels that the service user's independence should be encouraged. It is essential that both these views are acknowledged as being equally valid and important, and that a compromise is reached which will leave both workers feeling that they have made a contribution to the final actions agreed.

How to support service users in the exercise of their rights

One of the most useful and important things you can do for people is to give them information. Knowledge is power, and giving a person information empowers him or her. Working as a carer means that you are often going to be working with people who are vulnerable and who have no confidence or power. You will be able to support them very effectively by helping them to stand up for their rights. Many people you work with will be unaware of the information they need, because:

- ▶ they are unaware that the information exists
- ▶ they do not know how to find it
- ▶ there are physical barriers to accessing information
- ▶ there are emotional barriers to seeking information.

DID YOU KNOW?

Age Concern receives around 16,000 requests for information in a six-month period. When the figures were last analysed, around 25 per cent of the queries were found to be about health and social care, only slightly less about consumer issues (including wills), 10 per cent about financing residential care, and about 20 per cent respectively about income and housing.

If you are going to provide people with information, there are certain basic rules you must observe. There is no point in providing information which is out of date or inaccurate, or in giving people the right information at the wrong time.

Keys to good practice

✔ Make sure that your information is up to date. You may have to contact quite a few places to make sure you have the most accurate information possible. Check the dates on any leaflets you have and contact the producer of the leaflet to see whether it has been replaced.

✔ Go to the most direct source, wherever possible. For example, for information about benefits, contact the Benefits Agency. If you need to know about community care services, contact social services.

- ✔ Advice services such as the Citizens Advice Bureau are excellent and provide a wide range of information. Make use also of the specialist organisations which represent specific groups, such as Age Concern or Scope.
- ✔ Check whether the information you are providing has local, regional and national elements. For instance, if you are providing information about Age Concern's services for older people, it is important to provide the local contact as well as national contact points.
- ✔ The information you provide must be in a format that can be used by the person it is intended for. For example, there is little value in providing an ordinary leaflet to an individual with impaired vision. You will need to obtain large print, taped or braille versions depending on the way in which the individual prefers to receive information.
- ✔ Consider the language used and provide information in a language which the individual can easily understand. Information is of no value if it is misunderstood.
- ✔ Provide information at an appropriate time when the individual can make use of it. For example, a man who has just had a leg amputated, following an accident, will not be ready to receive information about the latest design in wheelchairs or how to join in sports for disabled people. He may be interested in 12 months' time, but initially he is going to need information about support groups, and practical information about how artificial limbs work, and how to manage to use the toilet!
- ✔ The information you provide must be relevant and useful. For example, if an individual wants to make a complaint to the Benefits Agency, you will need to find out what the complaints procedure is and provide the relevant information and forms to be completed. A general leaflet about the services of the Benefits Agency would not be as helpful.

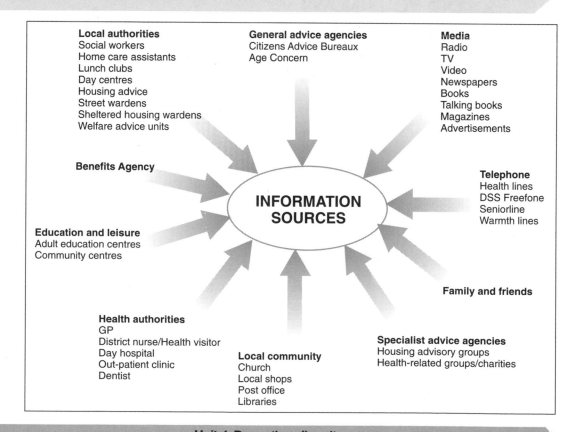

Sources of information.

Supporting people where needed

There may be occasions when you have identified a person's rights and given him or her the information needed. However, the individual may not be able to exercise those rights effectively. There can be many reasons why people miss out on their rights:

▶ their rights may be infringed by someone else
▶ there may be physical barriers
▶ there may be emotional barriers.

Where people cannot exercise their own rights, it is sometimes important that someone acts on their behalf. If it is within your work role to do so, you could act in a formal or informal way to assist.

Acting to help someone exercise his or her rights in a formal way may involve you speaking on that person's behalf to another agency, for example the Benefits Agency. Before you undertake this role you must check with your manager that it is appropriate for you to do so. Alternatively you may need to contact a professional advocate, such as a welfare rights worker or solicitor, in order to support service users.

You also need to be very sure that you are not assisting someone to exercise his or her rights because you are angered by an injustice. It must be because the individual, possibly based on information you have provided, wants to exercise his or her rights. The key when acting on behalf of another is to consult, and to constantly ensure that you are doing what he or she wishes.

CASE STUDY

Mrs S lives alone on just her state pension. She has never claimed any income support although there is no doubt she would be entitled to it. She struggles to survive on her pension and, by the time she has paid all her bills and fed the cat, there is little left for herself. She eats very little and is reluctant to turn the heating on. Despite being given all the relevant information by her home care assistant, Mrs S will not claim any further benefits. She always says: 'I shall be fine, there are others worse off than me. Let it go to those who need it.'

1 What are Mrs S's rights?
2 Should action be taken on her behalf?
3 Would the situation be different if she had a son with a learning disability who lived with her? Would her rights still be the same? Would her responsibilities still be the same?
4 What would your responsibilities be if you were a carer for Mrs S?

You may also need to defend people's rights in a more informal way during your normal work. For example, people have a right to privacy, and you may need to act to deal with someone who constantly infringes upon that by discussing other people's circumstances in public. You will have to balance the rights of one person against another, and decide whose rights are being infringed. You may decide that a right to privacy is more important than the right to free speech. That may be appropriate in your workplace, but does the same principle apply to politicians and the way they are discussed in the media?

Check it out

An individual's right to rest may be infringed by someone who shouts all night. How would you balance the rights of one person not to be disturbed against the rights of another not to be given medication which is only for the benefit of others?

Complaints

An important part of exercising rights is being able to complain if services are poor or do not meet expectations. All public service organisations are required to have a complaints procedure and to make the procedure readily available for people to use. Part of your role may be to assist service users in making complaints, either directly, by supporting them in following the procedure, or indirectly, by making sure that they are aware of the complaints procedure and are able to follow it.

Complaints to an organisation are an important part of the monitoring process and they should be considered as part of every review of service provision. If all service users simply put up with poor service and no one complains to an organisation, it will never be aware of where the service needs improvement.

What is empowerment?

Empowerment is about making sure that people are able to make choices, and that they can take control over as much of their lives as possible. Helping people make choices is a vital part of providing care as a service. Promoting empowerment simply means doing everything you can in your own practice and in your own work setting to make sure that this happens.

Many people who receive care services are unable to make many choices about their lives. This can be because of a range of different circumstances, but often it can be because of the way essential services are provided.

There are many choices which we take for granted – you can usually make basic choices in your life without even having to think about them. For example:

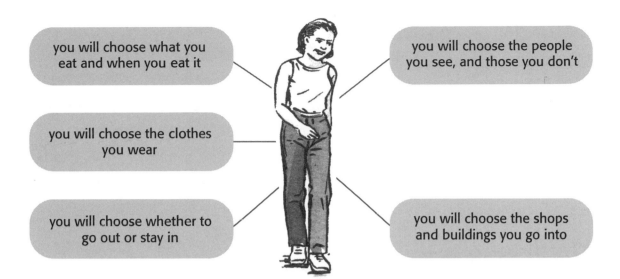

you will choose what you eat and when you eat it

you will choose the people you see, and those you don't

you will choose the clothes you wear

you will choose whether to go out or stay in

you will choose the shops and buildings you go into

Most of the time you give little thought to these choices. However, if you consider the service users in your own setting, you will realise that not all of them have the same options and choices as you do.

Check it out

For a couple of days, keep a list of the choices you make about everyday aspects of your life – use some of the examples above to start you off, but you will soon notice many more.

Now, think about the service users in your work setting. Write down next to each item on your list the names of service users who are also able to make the same choice. Do most service users have the same choices as you?

The importance of rights

Ensuring that all service users can exercise their rights is an essential part of the role of any worker in a care setting. If you are always conscious of the rights of those you care for, and always aware of the need to make sure those rights are not being infringed or denied, then you cannot fail to deliver a good quality service, and you will be on the road to developing into an excellent practitioner.

Outcome activity 1.1

You can do this activity by yourself, but it is better if you can work in a small group with three or four others.

Choose at least **three** different service users whose rights you will be able to investigate. These may be real service users from your workplace, or they may be relatives or friends. If you cannot find three people for your activity, then you may use up to two imaginary service users.

Make sure that each of the three has at least **one** major difference. This can be:

▶ age
▶ gender
▶ culture
▶ race
▶ level of disability
▶ type of disability
▶ type of service used
▶ any other significant difference.

Ask permission from the service users you are intending to include in your activity. Make sure that you do not identify individual service users during your activity, and explain to the service users that all information about them will remain confidential. You should refer to them by their initials or choose different names. The activity involves the following steps.

Step 1
Research the rights which each of your three service users has. All of them will have the same basic rights which we all have, but there will be some differences because of the significant differences in the service users you have chosen.

You can use a range of ways to find information about rights – the Internet is a useful method of research, along with textbooks. Make a note of all the websites you visit and each of the books you refer to.

Step 2
Discuss in your group, or think about, at least **two** situations for each service user where he or she would not be able to enjoy the rights you have identified. If you cannot clearly identify two situations for each service user, discuss situations which could result in the service user being unable to exercise his or her rights.

Step 3
Decide in your group, or think about, how the service users can be helped to exercise the rights you have identified. Consider the roles of each of the following:

▶ the government
▶ society as a whole
▶ the organisation providing care
▶ the individual workers providing care
▶ relatives and friends.

Step 4

Prepare a presentation showing what you have found out about your service users' rights, to be given to your tutor group, or your assessor(s), or a group of colleagues. The presentation can be prepared using handouts, overhead transparencies or using a computer programme such as PowerPoint, depending on the technology available. Plan a discussion after the presentation, using the information you have noted in Step 3.

Step 5

Deliver the presentation and lead the discussion on how to combat discrimination and how to help people exercise their rights without infringing the rights of others.

Develop methods of practice which enable the promotion of people's differences in a positive way

What is normal?

The notion of 'normality and abnormality' is very difficult to pin down. What is normal for one person is not for another. For instance, taking off your shoes when entering a holy place is normal for many people, but would be an unusual experience for others. For extended families to share a house is normal in some cultures and definitely not in others. Normality can only ever be 'normal' for a specific person – there is no such thing as a 'normal for everyone'. The particular set of circumstances always has to be considered.

As a society, we also identify 'normality' through statistics, surveys or a census. These methods identify facts about the population as a whole and demonstrate that a majority think or do something in a particular way. This can be interpreted as 'the norm' – although in fact it is actually a 'majority' or even an 'average' position. The danger of interpreting normality through statistics is that this misses out all the other factors which place normality in a context, such as culture, values, economics and beliefs. Statistics can be very useful when we want to find out a majority view, or to find out information about a whole group of people, but beware of the differences between a statistical 'norm' and 'normal'.

Self-esteem

Self-esteem is about how people value themselves and how they see themselves (their self-image). People have different levels of self-confidence, and it is very common to hear that somebody is not very confident or does not have a very high opinion of himself or herself.

The reasons why people have different levels of self-esteem are complex. The way people feel about themselves is often laid down during childhood. A child who is encouraged and regularly told how good he or she is and given a lot of positive feelings is the sort of person who is likely to feel that he or she has something to offer and can make a useful contribution to any situation. But a child who is constantly shouted at, blamed or belittled is likely to grow into an adult who lacks belief in himself or herself, or finds it difficult to go into new situations and to accept new challenges.

Not all the reasons for levels of self-confidence and self-image come from childhood. There are many experiences in adult life that can affect self-confidence and how people feel about themselves, for example:

▶ being made redundant
▶ getting divorced
▶ the death of somebody close
▶ the loss of independence, possibly having to go into residential care or into hospital
▶ the shock of being burgled

- ▶ being discriminated against
- ▶ having a bad fall, which results in a feeling of helplessness and a lack of self-worth.

All of these experiences can have devastating effects. Very often, people will become withdrawn and depressed as a result, and a great deal of support and concentrated effort is needed to help them through these very difficult situations.

Check it out

Look at the tree diagram above. It shows people at a great many stages and in a great many different situations. Study them all carefully.

1 Where do you think you fit? Are you the person at the top of the tree smiling, or the person near the top of the tree but not very happy? Are you falling, or being pushed? Are you hanging on by a thread or having great fun? Are you climbing up, or sliding down?
2 Which figures look the happiest?
3 Which figure would you most like to be?
4 Which figure would you least like to be? Why?

REMEMBER

The people you provide care for all see themselves at different stages on the tree, and have probably seen themselves at different stages at various points in their lives. Nobody stays at the same point on the tree forever. As circumstances change, so do people's views of themselves and how they fit in.

Self-concept

If self-esteem is about how we **value** ourselves, self-concept, or self-image, is about how we **see** ourselves. Both are equally important when you are working.

Self-concept is about what makes people who they are. Everyone has a concept of himself or herself – it can be a positive image overall or a negative one, but a great many factors contribute to an individual sense of identity. These will include:

▶ gender
▶ language/accent
▶ religion

▶ race
▶ values and beliefs
▶ sexual orientation.

All of these are aspects of our lives which contribute towards our idea of who we are. As a care worker it is essential that you consider how the service users you work with will have developed their own self-concept and identity and it is important that you recognise and promote this.

The values, beliefs, tastes and preferences which service users have are what makes them who they are, and must be supported, nurtured and encouraged, and not ignored and disregarded because they are inconvenient or don't fit in with the care system.

In your role as a care worker, you will come across situations where a little thought or a small change in practice could make people feel more valued and respected as individuals. For example, you may need to find out how a service user likes to be addressed. Is the use of the title 'Mr' or 'Mrs' considered more respectful and appropriate, or is a first name preferred? This, particularly for some older people, can be one of the ways of indicating respect that is felt to be important.

You will need to give thought to the values and beliefs which service users may have, for example:

▶ religious or cultural beliefs about eating certain foods
▶ values concerning forms of dress
▶ beliefs or preferences about who should be able to provide personal care.

All service users are different and will have different values and beliefs, including about what they prefer to eat.

What do you need to do?

You need to make sure that people have been asked about religious or cultural preferences and those preferences are recorded so that all care workers and others providing care are able to access them.

There may already be arrangements in your workplace to ask for and record this information. If so, you must ensure that you are familiar with the process and that you know where to find the information for every service user you work with. If your workplace does not have arrangements in place to find out about people's choices and preferences, you should discuss with your line manager ways in which you can help to find this out.

How do you need to do it?

The prospect of having to ask people questions about their background, values and beliefs can be daunting. But it is quite rare for people to be offended by your showing an interest in them! Simple, open questions, asked politely, are always the best way: 'Excuse me, Mr Khan, the information I have here notes that you are a Muslim. Can you tell me about any particular foods you do not wish to eat?'

You can obtain some information by observation. For instance, looking at someone can tell you a lot about his or her preferences in dress. Particular forms of clothing worn for religious or cultural reasons are usually obvious (a turban or a sari, for instance, is easy to spot) but other forms of dress may also give you some clues about the person wearing them. Think about how dress can tell you about the amount of money people are used to spending on clothes, or what kind of background they come from. Clothes also tell you a lot about someone's age and the type of lifestyle they are likely to be used to. Beware, however – any information you think you gain from this type of observation must be confirmed by checking your facts. Otherwise it is easy to be caught out – some people from wealthy backgrounds wear cheap clothes, and some people in their seventies wear the latest fashions and have face lifts!

Check it out

Look at the form, or other means of recording information, which is used in your workplace to set down the cultural or religious preferences of service users. Fill it in as if you were the service user. Now note down all the factors which make you who you are. Include your gender, age, background, economic and social circumstances, nationality, culture, religion, sexual orientation, and your preferences about food, entertainment, relaxation, reading material and so on.

Look at the form you have completed. Would it tell a care worker enough about you to ensure that you were able to be the same person you were before receiving a care service? If not, think about which other questions you need to be asked, and note them down. Make sure that, if appropriate, you ask these questions of service users.

Planning for individuals

The process of providing care should be carefully planned and designed to ensure that the service is exactly right for the individual it is meant to be helping. This is of key significance, not just because it is a right to which everyone is entitled, but also because health and well-being respond to emotional factors as much as physical ones. Service users will benefit to a great extent if the service they receive is centred around their own needs and the ways in which they wish these needs to be met. Feeling valued as a person is likely to improve the self-esteem and self-confidence of service users and contribute to an overall improvement in their health and well-being.

Check it out

Think of an occasion when you have felt really special – it may have been a special day, such as a birthday or wedding, or an achievement like winning an award or passing a test. Note down how you felt and try to recall the reasons why you felt special.

How to recognise your own prejudices

One of the hardest things to do is to acknowledge your own prejudices and how they affect what you do. Prejudices are a result of your own beliefs and values, and may often be in conflict with the situations you work in. There is nothing wrong with having your own beliefs and values – everyone has them, and they are a vital part of making you the person you are. But you must be aware of them, and how they may affect what you do at work.

Think about the basic principles which apply in your life. For example, you may have a basic belief that you should always be honest. Then think about what that could mean for the way you work – might you find it hard to be pleasant to someone who was found to have lied extensively? You may believe that abortion is wrong. Could you deal sympathetically with a woman who had had an abortion? You may have been brought up to take great care of people with disabilities and believe that they should be looked after and protected. How would you cope in an environment which encouraged people with disabilities to take risks and promoted their independence?

Check it out

Make a list of the things you believe in as values, and a second list of how they could affect your work. Then, examine whether they do affect your work – you may need the views of a trusted colleague or your supervisor to help you with this. This exercise is very hard, and it will take a long time to do. It is often better done over a period of time. As you become more aware of your own actions, you will notice how they have the potential to affect your work.

Treating people as individuals

You should always consult the individual before you carry out any procedure, and explain everything you do. Even if the procedure is part of his or her plan of care and has been done many times before, you should never take a person's agreement for granted.

Everyone should be offered choices wherever possible. This may be about when, where or how their care is provided. In circumstances where a choice is not possible, either because of an individual's circumstances or a lack of resources, this should be explained.

These are examples of the kinds of choice you may be able to offer to people when you provide care:

Care service	Choices
Personal hygiene	Bath, shower or bed bath
	Assistance or no assistance
	Morning, afternoon or evening
	Temperature of water
	Toiletries
Food	Menu
	Dining table or tray
	Timing
	Assistance
	In company or alone

Clearly, the range of choices will vary depending on the circumstances, but the principle remains the same – that people should not have care imposed on them without being able to be actively involved in the decisions about how and when care is delivered.

DID YOU KNOW?

One of the fears most frequently expressed by people who need to be cared for, particularly older people whose health has deteriorated or people who have been disabled through an accident or illness, is that they will lose their independence and will no longer be regarded as a person of any value.

Part of valuing people as individuals is having respect for all of the people you deal with. Respect is usually something which develops as you form relationships. When you provide care for someone, you will get to know and talk to him or her, and a relationship will grow. This is not easy with all individuals you care for. When there appears to be no two-way communication, you may find that forming a relationship is difficult. If you work with people who do not appear to relate to you, perhaps because they are very confused, because they have a very low level of functioning or even because they are not conscious, then it is easy to forget that they are still individuals and need to be treated as such.

Keys to good practice

✔ Make sure that any service which you provide for someone is with their agreement. People have a right to choose the care they receive and the way in which they receive it.

✔ You must make sure that each person you care for is treated in the same way, regardless of his or her ability to respond to you. This means talking to people who do not seem to understand you, and to people who may appear not to respond. You should explain everything you are doing and go through the details of any procedures you are carrying out.

REMEMBER

▶ Everyone has the right to make choices about care.
▶ All people are different.

Of course, you cannot suddenly stop doing and thinking things which you have been doing and thinking all your life, but you can develop an awareness of what you are doing and start to ask yourself questions about why you have acted in the way you have.

Once you realise how your own background and beliefs alter the way you think about people, you can begin to recognise the differences and see the value of other cultures and beliefs. It is inevitable that, by thinking carefully about what has influenced you, you will also consider what has influenced others with whom you come into contact.

You need to talk to people, whether they are colleagues or service users, about aspects of their culture or lifestyle you do not understand. As a care professional, it is your responsibility to make sure that you have considered the culture, beliefs and lifestyle of someone for whom you are providing care. It is not acceptable to expect that they will adapt to your set of cultural beliefs and expectations.

The diversity of the human race is what makes living in our society such a rich and varied experience. If you try to welcome this diversity, rather than resist, condemn or belittle the things you do not understand, you will find that your relationships with colleagues and service users will be much more rewarding and the quality of your care practice will be greatly improved.

Valuing others

Once you are aware of your own beliefs and values, and have recognised how important they are, you must think about how to accept the beliefs and values of others. The individuals you work with are all different, and so it is important to recognise and accept that diversity.

In the previous outcome, you looked at the rights which people can exercise under the law. This outcome is concerned with understanding the varied nature of human beings and how to ensure that the differences are valued and acknowledged.

Many workplaces now have policies which are about 'managing diversity' rather than 'equal opportunities'. This is because many people have realised that until diversity is recognised and valued, there is no realistic possibility of any policy about equal opportunities being really effective.

Check it out

1 This exercise is best done with a group of colleagues, but you can do it on your own – it just takes longer! Generate some ideas for a list of all the cultures and nationalities you can think of. Write them down. Next to each one, write something that the culture has given to the world. For example, the Egyptians gave mathematics, the Chinese developed some wonderful medicines, and so on.

  Next, think about people from the groups you care for. Note down the special angle of understanding each group can bring to society. For instance, someone who is visually impaired will always judge people on how they behave, not on how they look. Older people can often bring a different perspective to a situation based on years of experience and understanding.

2 In your own workplace, find out about the policy for ensuring equal opportunities, or for managing diversity. Make sure you read the policy. Consider whether you think it is being implemented.

Human needs

All human beings have needs which must be met in order for them to achieve comfort and the feeling of well-being.

There are different ways of looking at human needs, and we will consider two of them:

▶ PIES (Physical, Intellectual, Emotional and Social needs)
▶ Maslow's hierarchy of needs.

PIES

This is one of simplest ways to think about needs and to remember what they are, as the diagram below shows.

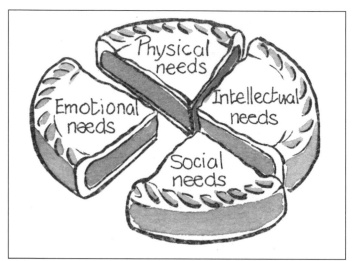

Human noods — PIES.

Physical needs

These are things like food, drink, warmth, shelter and sleep.

Physical needs are usually very basic, and it is impossible to survive without them. Of course, the needs will vary with the age of the individual and the stage of life he or she is at. But generally, human beings have a greater range of physical needs at the start of their lives and in old age. These tend to be the times when physical needs are greater than just food, warmth and shelter. At the beginning of life, a child requires assistance with moving, feeding and cleaning of body waste. Some or all of these needs may recur in the later stages of life.

Intellectual needs

This is not about being clever! Intellectual needs are about mental stimulation and having varied interests. Everyone needs to keep his or her brain active – this is not to suggest that everyone should try to be Einstein, but simply that all humans need to have something which holds their interest or makes them think. Like physical needs, intellectual needs change to fit the life stage: a baby will be stimulated by colours and simple shapes or by new sounds. But an older child or adolescent requires considerably more to prevent boredom! An adult will benefit from having interests and outlets which offer a challenge and a change. Later adulthood is a vital time to ensure that intellectual needs are met, as maintaining interests and having access to mental stimulation become increasingly important if physical abilities decline.

Emotional needs

Most people like to be liked; most people like to love and be loved. At the various stages of our lives, the needs will be different, but basically everyone needs to feel secure, nurtured and loved. A new-born child needs to feel safe and secure, or he or she will become distressed. As children grow, they benefit from receiving love and caring, as well as having boundaries, limits and routines which provide security. As adolescents progress into adulthood, emotional fulfilment is likely to come from developing a close emotional bond with another person. Throughout the life of most human beings the need to be emotionally contented is of great importance.

DID YOU KNOW?

Children who are deprived of love and affection become silent and withdrawn. They fail to thrive and have difficulty in developing normally.

Social needs

Social needs are about relationships with other people. No one lives in a vacuum, and most human beings like to relate to other human beings! As a species, we have never lived a solitary existence. Humans have always sought to meet their social needs by living in groups alongside others. All cultures have a history of people grouping together in villages and towns or simply in tribes or families.

Maslow's hierarchy of needs

This approach, one of the most useful, was suggested by the psychologist Abraham Maslow.

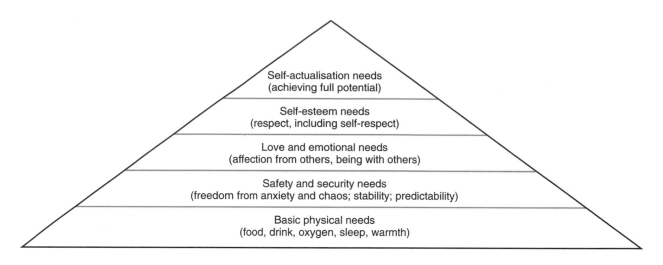

Maslow's hierarchy of needs: people need to satisfy the needs at the bottom of the triangle before going higher.

Basic physical needs

People will do whatever is necessary to meet their basic physical needs. These needs rank as the most important when people are placed under threat. Most people are fortunate enough to be able to take the basic physical needs for granted, but all human beings, if they are deprived of them, will go to great lengths to satisfy those needs. For example, if a person is starving it becomes his or her overriding priority to find food. All of the other higher-level needs fade into insignificance when compared to needs like food, warmth and shelter.

Safety and security needs

These are the needs which people will try to satisfy once they have met their basic needs. When they have sufficient food, some heat and a shelter, then they will look to feel safe and secure. Safety and security means different things to different people, but safety from physical danger is what most people will look for. Freedom from fear is something which is important to everyone, and individuals will try to achieve that and will see it as a higher priority than establishing relationships. Stability and security also include the need to live in a stable and unchaotic society. Humans need to be free from anxiety as well as from fear, and will take steps to try to regulate the environment in which they live to achieve this.

Love and emotional needs

Human beings need to reach out and form relationships with other human beings. They need to love and to be loved in return, to express affection and caring for others, and to feel cared for and nurtured in return. It is about more than having a close relationship which we would define as love. It is also about contacts with others – friends, colleagues, neighbours – and the opportunity to co-operate and work alongside others. Most individuals dislike feeling like outsiders or not being accepted by a group, and a failure to make relationships with others is likely to make people feel very badly about themselves. The need to form relationships with other human beings, however, only becomes important after basic needs and safety and security needs have been achieved.

Self-esteem needs

Self-esteem is about the way people feel about themselves. It is important that people feel they have a valuable contribution to make, whether it is to society as a whole or within a smaller area such as their local community, workplace or their own family.

Feeling good about yourself also has a great deal to do with your own experiences throughout your life and the kind of confidence that you were given as you grew up. All human beings need to feel that they have a valuable place and a valuable contribution to make within society.

Self-esteem is discussed in detail on pages 28–29.

Self-actualisation needs

This is about every human being's need to reach his or her maximum potential. This might be through setting out to achieve new goals or meeting new challenges, or through developing existing talents. Abraham Maslow suggests that if our other needs have not been met (from the most basic needs up to self-esteem needs), then this need will never be met, because people will continue to try to achieve the needs lower down the hierarchy, and will never attempt self-fulfilment and never reach their full potential.

REMEMBER

Maslow may be right in his hierarchy of needs. Think about the number of times that you have seen people who are confused, depressed, dirty and malnourished who, within a few days of having their basic needs of warmth and food met, have started to make relationships and to try to meet some of their higher needs.

CASE STUDY

Miss J had lived alone in a very large, cold house since her mother died about 15 years ago. She was always viewed as a bit odd by the local neighbours. She appeared quite grubby and unkempt and never spoke to or smiled at anyone. She was very thin, and seemed to be just skin and bone. The milkman and paper girl, who were the only people who ever went to the house, said that it looked very messy and dirty inside and there was never any evidence of heating, even in the depths of winter.

She was admitted to hospital one day after the milkman looked through the window and saw her on the floor when she didn't answer his knock. She had fallen and fractured her femur.

At first, Miss J didn't speak to anyone apart from asking to be left alone. She agreed to a bed bath and having her hair washed, and ate the meals which were brought to her. The nurses and health care assistants noticed that after about a week, she began to respond to their conversation and seemed to look forward to having a shower and eating her meals. Gradually, she began to talk to other patients on the ward and it became clear that she was a well-informed and intelligent woman with a keen sense of humour.

When she was ready for discharge, she decided to go on to convalescence and to sell her house and buy a flat in a retirement community, where she would meet other people and yet retain her independence.

1 Which of Miss J's needs were met by coming into hospital?
2 What effect did that have on her behaviour?
3 What next level needs is Miss J going to meet?
4 What may have happened if she had not had the fall?

Planning to meet different needs and wants

When an individual either requests, or is referred for a service, the assessment and planning cycle begins. Throughout the consultation and planning which follows, the individual and his or her needs should be at the centre of the process. You will need to make sure that service users have every opportunity to state exactly how they wish their needs to be met. Some service users will be able to give this information personally; others will need an advocate who will support them in expressing their views.

Developing relationships

Communication is the basis of all relationships, regardless of whether the relationships are personal or professional. As individuals communicate, a relationship is formed. This is usually a two-way process as each individual involved gets to know the other through a process of communicating and sharing information.

When you provide care for someone, you will get to know and talk to him or her, and a relationship will grow. This is not easy with all individuals you care for. When there appears to be little communication, you may find that forming a relationship is difficult.

Stages of an interaction

Communication between individuals in called an 'interaction'. As you spend time in communication with someone, the nature of the interaction will go through changes.

Body language and non-verbal communication are always important.

▶ *Stage 1:* Introduction, light and general. At first, the content of the communication may be of little significance. This is the stage at which both parties decide whether they want to continue the discussion, and how comfortable they feel. Body language and non-verbal communication are very important at this stage.

▶ *Stage 2:* Main contact, significant information. The middle of any interaction is likely to contain the 'meat', and this is where you will need to use active listening skills to ensure that the interaction is beneficial.

▶ *Stage 3:* Reflect, wind up, end positively. People often have the greatest difficulty in knowing how to end an interaction. Ending in a positive way where all participants are left feeling that they have benefited from the interaction is very important. You may find that you have to end an interaction because of time restrictions, or you may feel that enough has been covered – the other person may need a rest, or you may need a break!

At the end of an interaction you should always try to reflect on the areas you have covered, and offer a positive and encouraging ending, for example: 'I'm glad you have talked about how unhappy you have been feeling. Now we can try to work at making things better.'

Even if the content of an interaction has been fairly negative, you should encourage the individual to see the fact that the interaction has taken place as being positive in itself.

If you are called away before you have had a chance to properly 'wind up' an interaction with an individual, make a point of returning to end things in a positive way. If you say 'I'll be back in a minute', make sure that you do go back.

Communication with service users

The principles of good communication are an important part of making sure that the service user is fully a part of the plans for any service provided.

The consequences of not planning service delivery around the needs of those who receive it can be far reaching, as shown in the table on the next page.

Need/wish of service user	Ways to meet need	Possible effects of not taking account of need
Food prepared according to religious or cultural beliefs	Ensure that service is provided by people who have been trained to prepare food correctly	Food not eaten so health deteriorates. Other services refused Food eaten out of necessity but in extreme distress
To receive residential care but maintain social contacts	Provide transport to visit friends and for friends to visit	Service user becomes isolated and depressed
Take control of own arrangements for personal care	Discuss and support the planning of direct payments	Service user loses self-esteem and becomes disempowered

The impact of practising in a way which makes people feel valued is enormous. Often the steps are small and do not take a great deal of effort or demand major changes – but the results are so effective that any effort you have made will be repaid many times over by the positive benefits for the service users you care for.

Outcome activity 1.2

Welcome House is a resource centre providing residential and supported living accommodation along with community care for older people. It is in a city which has a very varied ethnic and racial make-up. Large numbers of people from many different cultural and racial backgrounds live in the area. Some have been there for many years, large numbers were born in the area and others have recently arrived in the country.

You have been asked to produce a guide which will help new members of staff to become familiar with the range of different cultures, values and beliefs among service users. You can do this alone, but it is better if you can work in a small group.

Step 1
Plan how to produce your guide. You could produce a paper booklet or information folder, word processed and with illustrations, or you could produce an on-line guide on a computer. You will need to make sure that the format you choose is accessible for the people who may use the guide.

After deciding on the format of your guide, decide what to include in it. Remember that this is for staff who may not be familiar with any of the cultural needs of some of the service users.

Step 2
Carry out the research for your guide. You will need to find out about the different needs of people who come from different cultural and racial backgrounds.

Step 3
Produce your guide using the planned format. When it is complete, show it to your supervisor, tutor and assessor and, if possible, to service users and ask for their feedback on how useful they think it would be.

Everyone has their own set of values, beliefs and preferences. You will have your own. It is an essential part of making you who you are. What you believe in, what you see as important and what you see as acceptable or desirable are as much a part of your personality as whether you are shy, outgoing, funny, serious, friendly or reserved.

People who work caring for others need to be more aware than most of how their work can be affected by their own beliefs.

REMEMBER

If you are working in a factory producing electronic chips, the production line will continue to operate regardless of whether you view your job as interesting or boring. It will still continue if you shout abuse at it – your opinion will have no effect on the end result of the work. As long as you continue to play your part in the process, the chips will be turned out and the job will be completed satisfactorily.

If you work in a library, people will continue to borrow and read books that you consider boring, poorly written or distasteful. With the exception of a small number of those who might ask your advice, most of the people for whom you provide a service will remain unaware of your beliefs, interests or values.

Exploring your own values, interests and beliefs

The way in which you respond to people is linked to what you believe in, what you consider important and the things that interest you. You may find that you react positively to people who share your values and less warmly to people who choose to have different priorities. When you develop friendships it is natural to spend time with people who share your interests and values, those who are 'on your wavelength'. If you are a person who enjoys a night out where there is plenty of lively activity, pop music and dancing, you are not likely to choose to spend time with someone whose perfect evening is to stay in with a bottle of wine and listen to opera. Everyone is different, and while you can recognise and respect the enjoyment that someone may achieve from an evening with Mozart, you may not choose to share it or feel that you have much in common.

Being able to choose friends and meet with others who share your interests is one of life's joys and pleasures, but the professional relationships you develop with people you care for are formed on an entirely different basis. As a professional carer you are required to provide the same quality of care for all, not just for those who share your views and beliefs. This may seem obvious, but knowing what you need to do and achieving it successfully are not the same thing.

You may believe that you treat everyone in the same way, but there can often be differences in approach or attitude of which you may be unaware. For example, you may spend more time with someone who is asking your advice about a course of action which you think is sensible than you would with someone who wanted to do something you considered inadvisable. There are many ways in which your beliefs, interests and values can affect how you relate to people. Some examples are shown in the table below.

Your beliefs/ values/interests	Situation	Possible effect
People have a responsibility to look after their own health	You are caring for someone with heart disease who continues to smoke and eats a lot of fried foods and cream cakes	You find it difficult to be sympathetic when she complains about her condition, and make limited responses
War and violence are wrong and people who fight should not be glorified as heroes	An elderly service user constantly recalls his days as a soldier and wants you to admire his bravery and that of his comrades	You try to avoid spending time chatting with him, and limit your contact to providing physical care
Chart and disco music	You visit a service user who constantly plays country and western music very loudly	You find it hard not to ask her to turn it down or off. You hurry through your work and your irritation shows in your body language

Hello, I am pleased to meet you.

There are many other situations in which you may find you are behaving differently towards different people. There is nothing unusual in this – in fact the only way to behave identically towards everyone is to be a robot!

However, it is important that you are aware of it, because it can make a difference to the quality of your work. Being aware of the factors that have influenced the development of your personality is not as easy as it sounds. You may feel that you know yourself very well, but knowing *who* you are is not the same as knowing *how* you got to be you.

Getting to know yourself.

Unravelling these influences is never easy, and you are not being asked to carry out an in-depth analysis of yourself – simply to begin to realise how your development has been influenced by a series of factors.

Factors which influence our development

Everyone's values and beliefs are affected to different degrees by the same range of factors. These include:

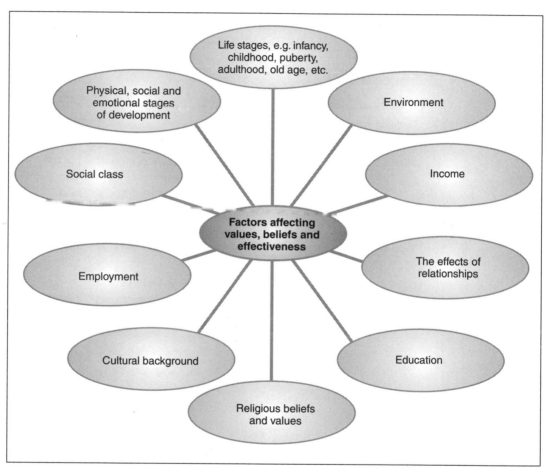

Various factors affect the way we develop.

Each of us will be influenced to a greater or lesser degree by some or all of those factors. As each individual is different the combination of factors and the extent of their influence will be different for each person. It is therefore important that you have considered and reflected on those factors which have influenced your development so that you understand how you became the person you are.

Life stages and development

One of the most significant influences is the life stage which people are at. Most people who are working in care are likely to fall into the young or middle adult group. If you look at those parts of the chart on the following pages, you should be able to see the stages of development which apply to your age group. The chart will have other important uses in helping you to understand the life stages service users are either at, or have experienced.

	Intellectual/cognitive	Social/emotional	Language	Physical
Infant, birth–1 year	Learns about new things by feeling with hands and mouth objects encountered in immediate environment	Attaches to parent(s), begins to recognise faces and smile; at about 6 months begins to recognise parent(s) and expresses fear of strangers, plays simple interactive games like peekaboo	Vocalises, squeals, and imitates sounds, says 'dada' and 'mama'	Lifts head first then chest, rolls over, pulls to sit, crawls and stands alone. Reaches for objects and rakes up small items, grasps rattle
Toddler, 1–2 years	Extends knowledge by learning words for objects in environment	Learns that self and parent(s) are different or separate from each other, imitates and performs tasks, indicates needs or wants without crying	Says some words other than 'dada' and 'mama', follows simple instructions	Walks well, kicks, stoops and jumps in place, throws balls. Unbuttons clothes, builds tower of 4 cubes, scribbles, uses spoon, picks up very small objects
Pre-school, 2–5 years	Understands concepts such as tired, hungry and other bodily states, recognises colours, becomes aware of numbers and letters	Begins to separate easily from parent(s), dresses with assistance, washes and dries hands, plays interactive games like tag	Names pictures, follows directions, can make simple sentences of two or three words, vocabulary increases	Runs well, hops, pedals tricycle, balances on one foot. Buttons clothes, builds tower of 8 cubes, copies simple figures or letters, for example O, begins to use scissors
School age, 5–12 years	Develops understanding of numeracy and literacy concepts, learns relationship between objects and feelings, acquires knowledge and understanding	Acts independently, but is emotionally close to parent(s), dresses without assistance, joins same-sex play groups and clubs	Defines words, knows and describes what things are made of, vocabulary increases	Skips, balances on one foot for 10 seconds, overestimates physical abilities. Draws person with 6 parts, copies detailed figures and objects

	Intellectual/cognitive	Social/emotional	Language	Physical
Adolescent, 12–18 years	Understands abstract concepts like illness and death, develops understanding of complex concepts	Experiences rapidly changing moods and behaviour, interested in peer group almost exclusively, distances from parent(s) emotionally, concerned with body image, experiences falling in and out of love	Uses increased vocabulary, understands more abstract concepts such as grief	May appear awkward and clumsy while learning to deal with rapid increases in size due to growth spurts
Young adult, 18–40 years	Fully developed, continues to develop knowledge base related to education or job	Becomes independent from parent(s), develops own lifestyle, selects a career, copes with career, social and economic changes and social expectations, chooses a partner, learns to live co-operatively with partner, becomes a parent	Fully developed	Fully developed
Middle age 40–65 years	Fully developed	Builds social and economic status, is fulfilled by work or family, copes with physical changes of ageing, children grow and leave nest, deals with ageing parents, copes with the death of parents	Fully developed	Begins to experience physical changes of ageing
Older adult, 65+ years	Fully developed	Adjusts to retirement, adjusts to loss of friends and relatives, copes with loss of spouse, adjusts to new role in family, copes with dying	Fully developed	Experiences more significant physical changes associated with ageing

Some of the key influences on your growth and development can be classified as belonging to your environment:

You may also have been affected by the social class to which you belonged.

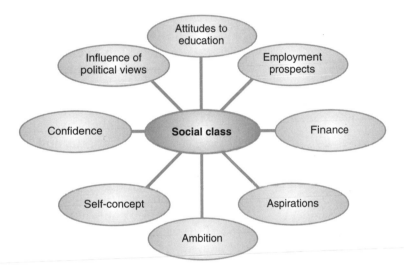

Consider also your cultural background and how this could have affected your development.

Construct spider diagrams for each of the factors which have influenced your development, and from those begin to identify which factors have exercised the greatest influence on you. This exercise should help you to identify what has affected the development of your own personality and abilities and how this may affect the way in which you work.

Factors affecting your practice

Once you have begun to identify the major factors which have influenced your development, the next stage is to look at how they have affected the way in

I really shouldn't have spoken to Mr Khan in that way. I'm absolutely hopeless at dealing with people. I'll have to get it right.

You need to think about how you can improve work practices to become more effective.

which you work and relate both to service users and colleagues. This is the basis of developing into a **reflective practitioner** (see Unit 3, page 136, for more on this). Working in care requires that in order to be an effective practitioner and to provide the best possible service for those you care for, you need to be able to reflect on what you do and the way you work and to identify your strengths and your weaknesses. It is important that you learn to use reflection on your own practice in a constructive way. Reflection should not be used to undermine your confidence in your own work; rather you should use it in a constructive way to identify areas which require improvement. The ability to do this is an indication of excellent practice. Any workers in care who believe that they have no need to improve their practice or to develop and add to their skills and understanding are not demonstrating good and competent practice, but rather an arrogant and potentially dangerous lack of understanding of the nature of work in the care sector.

Becoming a reflective practitioner is not about torturing yourself with self-doubts and examining your weaknesses until you reach the point where your self-confidence is at zero! But it is important that you examine the work that you have done and identify areas where you know you need to carry out additional development. A useful tool in learning to become a reflective practitioner is to develop a checklist which you can use, either after you have dealt with a difficult situation or at the end of each shift or day's work, to look at your performance.

Reflective practice checklist

1   How did I approach work?
2   Was my approach positive?
3   How did the way I worked affect the service users?
4   How did the way I worked affect my colleagues?
5   Did I give my work 100 per cent?
6   Which was the best aspect of the work I did?
7   Which was the worst aspect of the work I did?
8   Was this work the best I could do?
9   Are there any areas in which I could improve?
10 What are they, and how will I tackle them?

Getting feedback

It is sometimes difficult to take a step back and look at whether your working practices have improved as a result of training, development and increasing experience. So it is very important to seek out and act on feedback from an appropriate person, usually your supervisor.

Asking for feedback on your performance is not always easy – and listening to it can be harder! All of us find it difficult to hear feedback at times, especially if

Mirror, mirror on the wall...

we are being told we could do things better. However, you should learn to welcome feedback. Try to think of it as looking in a mirror. You probably never go out without looking in the mirror to check how you look. Think of professional feedback in the same way – how will you know how you are performing if you haven't asked anyone who is in a position to tell you?

Don't forget that you can ask for feedback from service users and colleagues too, not only from your supervisor.

Quality working

It is only by regularly evaluating your own practice that you will be sure that you are working to the highest possible standards, and meeting all of the requirements for quality provision, such as those laid out in national standards. As you grow more aware of the factors influencing people's development and the different influences on their lives, you will appreciate the rich diversity of people you work with. You will also be in a better position to support them, for example by informing them about cultural centres or self-help groups that may be appropriate.

The central theme and underpinning principle of care provision is that the service is centred on the person receiving it and not on those providing it. The

As you learn more about service users, you will be in a better position to give them appropriate information.

Care Standards Act 2000 put into law the concept of monitoring and regulating service providers to make sure that services are meeting the needs of the individuals for whom they are provided.

The Act established the National Care Standards Commission, which is responsible for implementing the National Minimum Standards across a wide range of care providers. The Commission inspects and regulates over 40,000 different establishments. Each type of care provider has a set of National Minimum Standards which it must meet, and against which it is regularly inspected.

In this way, service users are assured that the service they receive is of good quality, and also that all of those working in care settings have standards of performance. These are laid out in the National Occupational Standards which form the basis of the National Vocational Qualifications (NVQs)

Most workplaces are now also involved in Quality Assurance schemes and programmes, which recognise the performance of the organisation against externally agreed benchmarks. The National Occupational Standards are an excellent set of benchmarks for measuring performance, but there are others such as those which recognise particular areas of achievement, for example investment in training and staff development.

Outcome activity 1.3

Over a period of two weeks, collect at least **six** newspaper or magazine cuttings, or print out items from web-based news sites, about controversial or difficult issues. The cuttings can be about anything which has caught your interest – they do not have to be related to care, but they can be. **Three** of the cuttings must be articles which you agree with or think are right. **Three** of the cuttings must be items which describe actions or attitudes you disagree with or think are wrong. Go through each of your cuttings carefully and work out the reasons why you agreed or disagreed with the content.

The next steps should be carried out in a small group. If you are not working with a group of other candidates, then ask your supervisor, assessor or work colleagues to help you.

Step 1
Working in a small group, each person should identify a cutting he or she agrees with and explain to the group why. Each should then identify a cutting that he or she disagrees with and explain the reasons. Continue until all the cuttings have been considered.

Step 2

As a group, discuss the cuttings and look at the different reasons for agreement and disagreement. One person in the group should keep notes about the subjects discussed and the views expressed.

Step 3

On your own, prepare a reflective account on what this exercise has shown you about why you hold the values and beliefs you do. Include the following in the account:

▶ the values and beliefs you identified
▶ any which may seem to contradict each other – for example, you may believe in equal opportunities, but think that people seeking political asylum should not be allowed into the country
▶ what you learned about the influences on your values and beliefs
▶ the effects you think your own values and beliefs could have on the work you do.

Step 4

Share your account with your group and tutor or supervisor, and discuss the issues it raises.

For many people, working in care means coming to terms with the fact that some service users will be subjected to abuse by those who are supposed to care for them. For others it will not be the first time that they have been close to an abuse situation, either through personal experience or previous professional involvement.

Regardless of previous experience, coming face to face with situations where abuse is, or has been, taking place is difficult and emotionally demanding. Knowing what you are looking for, and how to recognise it, is an important part of ensuring that you are making the best possible contribution to protecting service users from abuse. Taking the right steps when faced with an abusive situation is the second part of your key contribution to service users who are, or have been, abused.

The forms of abuse which you will need to be aware of and to understand are abuses which are suffered by service users at the hands of someone who is providing care for them. This outcome is not about abuse by strangers, which needs to be dealt with in the same way as any other crime.

What is abuse?

Abuse takes place where one person exercises power in a harmful and negative way over another. The abuser can be anyone who has caring responsibilities for the service user – this includes professional and informal carers. A wide range of people can provide different types of care for a service user, whether he or she is an adult or a child. The table shows some examples.

Professional/formal carer	Informal carer
Care assistant	Parent
Social worker	Step-parent
Nurse	Son/daughter
Doctor	Sister/brother
Health visitor	Grandchild
Physiotherapist	Grandparent
Occupational therapist	Other relative
Ambulance crew	Friend
Hospital porter	Neighbour
Health centre staff	Volunteer
Probation officer	
Teacher	
Nursery worker/nanny	

People who are providing care are likely to be in a powerful position in relation to the service user. Some service users are more vulnerable than others, and this is, to some extent, related to their individual needs and circumstances. Someone who is frail, confused and lives alone is potentially vulnerable to some forms of abuse such as physical, sexual or emotional abuse. Someone who has profound learning difficulties or is confused is also more vulnerable to financial abuse.

People who abuse others do so as a result of misusing their power. Instead of recognising that the strength they have in relation to the service user is a positive thing which should be used to provide support and protection, they use their position in order to exercise power and control over others, in a way which is damaging and dangerous.

Naturally, if you are providing care for someone, you are likely to be physically stronger and more powerful than that person. You may be able to exert power because of your professional role and the tasks you undertake for the service user; it is also possible that your role places you in a position of authority which may intimidate the service user. It may be that you have greater intellectual ability than the service users you care for, or that they are in a position where they are totally dependent on you for their day-to-day personal care. Whatever the nature of the role which places a carer in a position of authority and power, the misuse of that position is a betrayal of trust and service users must be protected from it.

Abuse in a care setting

Abuse that occurs in a care setting may not be at the hands of members of staff. There is also abuse which comes about because of the way in which an establishment is run, where the basis for planning the systems, rules and regulations is not the welfare, rights and dignity of the residents or patients, but the convenience of the staff and management. This is the sort of situation where people can be told when to get up and go to bed, given communal clothing, only allowed medical attention at set times and not allowed to go out. This is referred to as 'institutional abuse'.

No dear, you can't go out now, you nearly slipped last time. You can't go on your own and I don't have anyone to send with you - can't you see how busy we all are?

Care settings include residential homes and hospitals, but people are cared for in many other situations: children are cared for by their parents, by a childminder, in nursery or school, in a youth group or in foster homes. Vulnerable adults can be cared for in supported living schemes, at home with informal carers or professional carers, with relatives and in day care, as well as in residential or nursing homes.

Forms of abuse

Abuse is about more than being hit or sexually assaulted. Of course, they are the most violent and obvious forms of abuse, and they may be the ones which are easier to identify. But there are other ways in which people can be abused, as the diagram below shows.

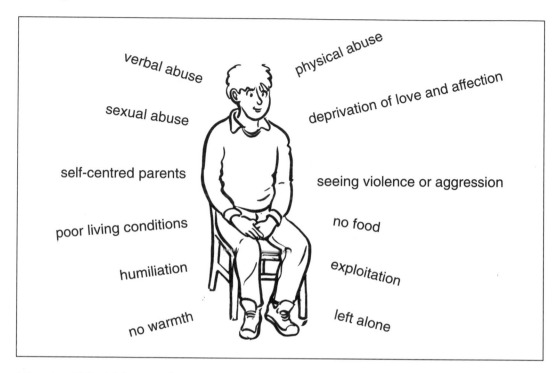

Ways in which children can be abused.

Children can be abused:

▶ emotionally, by being deprived of love or physical contact or by being constantly belittled and humiliated
▶ verbally, by being constantly shouted at
▶ by having to witness violent or aggressive scenes at home
▶ by being parented by people who are unable to put their child's needs before their own
▶ by being physically neglected, or living in filthy conditions
▶ by being deprived of food, warmth or shelter
▶ by being left without adult protection, to fend for themselves
▶ at the hands of other children, by being bullied at school or in the local neighbourhood
▶ by being exploited for sexual purposes or financial gain
▶ by those who use or purchase materials for the production of which children were exploited.

DID YOU KNOW?

Childline, the helpline for children, receives 10 attempted calls every minute.

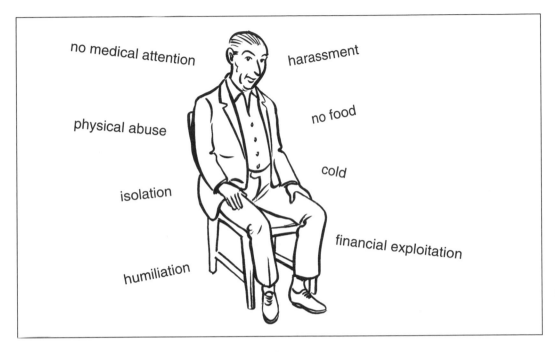

Ways in which vulnerable adults can be abused.

Vulnerable adults can also be abused. The broad definition of a 'vulnerable adult', according to government guidelines, is a person 'who is or may be in need of community care services by reason of mental or other disability, age or illness; and who is or may be unable to take care of himself or herself, or unable to protect himself or herself against significant harm or exploitation'.

The guidelines are called 'No Secrets: Guidance on developing and implementing multi-agency policies and procedures to protect vulnerable adults from abuse', and are published by the Department of Health and the Home Office. They define abuse as 'a violation of an individual's human and civil rights by any other person or persons'.

Abuse may consist of a single act or repeated acts. It may be physical, verbal or psychological, it may be a deliberate act of neglect or a failure to act, or it may occur when a vulnerable person is persuaded to enter into a financial or sexual act to which he or she has not given or cannot give informed consent.

▶ **Physical abuse** includes hitting, slapping, pushing, kicking, misuse of medication or restraint, or inappropriate sanctions.
▶ **Sexual abuse** includes rape and sexual assault or sexual acts to which the vulnerable adult has not consented, or could not consent, or was pressured into consenting.

- **Psychological abuse** includes emotional abuse, threats of harm or abandonment, deprivation of contact, humiliation, blaming, controlling, intimidation, coercion, harassment, verbal abuse, isolation or withdrawal from services or supportive networks.
- **Financial or material abuse** includes theft, fraud, exploitation, pressure in connection with wills, property or inheritance or financial transactions, or the misuse or misappropriation of property, possessions or benefits.
- **Neglect and acts of omission** include ignoring medical or physical care needs; failure to provide access to appropriate health, social care or educational services; and the withholding of the necessities of life, such as medication, adequate nutrition and heating.
- **Discriminatory abuse** includes racist and sexist abuse, abuse based on a person's disability, and other forms of harassment, slurs or similar treatment.

Any of these types of abuse may be the result of deliberate intent, negligence or ignorance.

Check it out

How many types of abuse does your workplace have guidelines to deal with? Look at the policy and procedures for dealing with abuse. See how many types of abuse are listed and what the procedures are. Ask your supervisor if you cannot find any information.

Self-harm

The one abuser it is very hard to protect someone from is himself or herself. Individuals who self-harm will be identified in their plan of care, and responses to their behaviour will be recorded. You must ensure that you follow the agreed plan for provision of care for someone who has a history of self-harm. It is usual that an individual who is at risk of harming himself or herself will be closely supported and you may need to contribute towards activities or therapies which have been planned for the individual.

Institutional abuse

Institutional abuse is not only confined to the large-scale physical or sexual abuse scandals of the type which are regularly publicised in the media. Of course this type of systematic and organised abuse goes on in residential and hospital settings, and must be recognised and dealt with appropriately so that service users can be protected. However, service users can be abused in many other ways in settings where they could expect to be cared for and protected. For example:

- service users in residential settings are not given choice over day-to-day decisions such as mealtimes, bedtimes, etc.
- freedom to go out is limited by the institution
- privacy and dignity are not respected

- personal correspondence is opened by staff
- the setting is run for the convenience of staff, not service users
- excessive or inappropriate sedation/medication are given
- access to advice and advocacy is restricted or not allowed
- complaints procedures are deliberately made unavailable.

Who can abuse?

Abuse can take place at home or in a formal care setting. At home, it could be an informal carer who is the abuser, although it could be a neighbour or regular visitor. It can also be a professional care worker who is carrying out the abuse. This situation can mean that abuse goes undetected for some time because of the unsupervised nature of a carer's visits to someone's home.

In a formal care setting, abuse may be more likely to be noticed, although some of the more subtle forms of abuse, such as humiliation, can sometimes be so commonplace that it is not recognised as abusive behaviour.

Abuse is not only carried out by individuals; groups or even organisations can also create abusive situations. It has been known that groups of carers in residential settings can abuse individuals in their care. Often people will act in a different way in a group than they would alone. Think about teenage 'gangs' which exist because people are prepared to do things jointly which they would not think to do if they were by themselves.

REMEMBER

Abusers can be:

- individuals
- groups
- organisations.

CASE STUDY

Julie was 43, and she had worked as a senior support worker in a residential unit for people with a learning disability for the past five years. Julie loved her job and was very committed to the residents in the unit. She was very concerned for the welfare of the people she supported and did everything she could for them. Many of them had been in the unit for many years and Julie knew them well. The unit was not very large and had only a small staff who were able to work very closely with the resident group.

Julie and the other staff were concerned that the residents could easily be taken advantage of, as some were not able to make effective judgments about other people and potentially risky situations.

Regular mealtimes were arranged so that everyone could share the day's experiences and talk together, and bedtimes and getting-up times were also strictly adhered to. The staff found that this was a good way of keeping the residents organised and motivated. Residents did not go out into the local town in the evenings because of the potential safety risk, but the staff would plan evenings of TV watching, choosing programmes which they thought would interest the residents. Sometimes simple games sessions or walks in the local park were arranged.

A new manager was appointed to the unit and Julie and the other staff were very surprised to find that this new manager was horrified by many of these practices, and wanted to make major changes.

1 What changes do you think the manager may have suggested?
2 Why do you think those changes may be needed?
3 Do you consider that Julie and the other staff members were practising in the best way for the residents?
4 Think about, or discuss, whether this situation was abusive.

You can probably begin to see that the different types of abuse are often interlinked, and service users can be victims of more than one type of abuse. Abuse is a deliberate act – it is something which someone actively does in order to demonstrate power and authority over another person. It is also done with the motive of providing some sort of gratification for the abuser.

What is neglect?

Neglect is very different from abuse. Whereas abuse involves a deliberate act, neglect happens when care is not given and a service user suffers as a result. The whole area of neglect has many associated issues and aspects you need to take into account, but there are broadly two different types of neglect:

▶ self-neglect
▶ neglect by others.

Self-neglect

Many people neglect themselves; this can be for a range of reasons. People may be ill or depressed and unable to make the effort, or not feel capable of looking after themselves. Sometimes people feel that looking after themselves is unimportant. Others choose to live in a different way from most people, one that does not match up to the expectations of others. Working out when someone is neglecting himself or herself, given all of these considerations, can be very difficult.

Self-neglect can show itself in a range of ways:

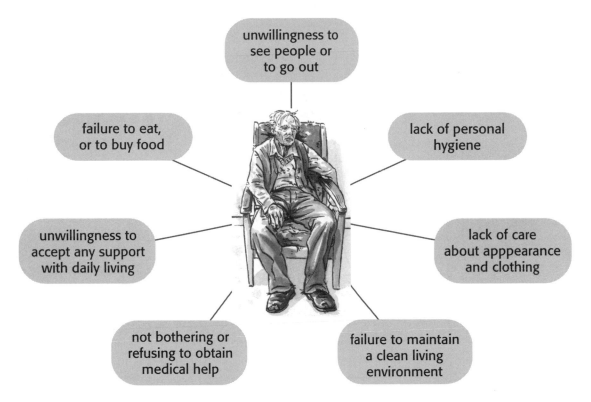

- unwillingness to see people or to go out
- lack of personal hygiene
- failure to eat, or to buy food
- unwillingness to accept any support with daily living
- lack of care about apppearance and clothing
- not bothering or refusing to obtain medical help
- failure to maintain a clean living environment

However, what may appear to be self-neglect may, in fact, be an informed choice made by someone who does not regard personal and domestic cleanliness or hygiene as priorities. It is always important to make a professional judgement based on talking with the service user and finding out his or her wishes, before making any assumptions about what may be needed.

Attempting to force someone to accept help with domestic and personal cleanliness when he or she has made a clear choice to live in an environment which differs from what is generally acceptable, would directly contravene the value base of care work. This value base supports the rights of service users to make choices in respect of their lives. However, issues can arise when the ways of living chosen by a service user have a direct impact on the lives of others. This is more likely to happen in the community, but it is also possible that such situations can occur in a residential environment, if, for example, a service user refuses to wash.

Situations like these are difficult to deal with, and it is important to think through the reasons why action may be necessary – or why action may seem to be necessary, but may not be justified on further consideration.

It may be hard to imagine the kind of tensions and conflicting views you may come across. Look at the following case study for an example.

CASE STUDY

B is 75, and he has lived alone since his wife died two years ago. Both he and his wife were academic writers and they were never very sociable or friendly with neighbours. They had no children and did not appear to have any friends. The house and garden had always been dilapidated and very untidy, and this appeared to have become worse since B's wife died. Neighbours contacted Social Services because they felt that B was neglecting himself. He very rarely went out to the shops and appeared very thin and unkempt. When social workers visited him, his house was dirty and there was very little food in the cupboards. He was dirty and his clothes were unwashed. B agreed to be visited by a psychiatrist. She could find no evidence of mental illness − in fact she described B as an intelligent and articulate man. B politely explained to all his visitors that he did not see the point in washing, he was unconcerned about food and was not bothered if he should die or become ill as a result of his actions.

1 What issues are raised in the case of B?
2 Discuss these with your colleagues or supervisor, or make notes on them. How would you resolve them?

Check it out

Ask one of your experienced colleagues, or your supervisor, if he or she can recall a situation where a service user had made a choice about lifestyle which gave others a cause for concern. Ask the following questions:

1 Why was the service user's choice a problem for the professional carers?
2 What are the problems created when service users adopt a risky lifestyle?
3 How was the situation resolved?

Neglect by others

This occurs when a professional or informal carer is caring for a service user and the needs of the service user are not met. Neglect can happen because those responsible for providing the care do not realise its importance, or because they cannot be bothered, or choose not, to provide it. As the result of neglect, service users can become ill, hungry, cold, dirty, injured or deprived of their rights. Neglecting someone you are supposed to be caring for can mean failing to undertake a range of care services, for example:

▶ not providing adequate food
▶ not providing assistance with eating food if necessary
▶ not ensuring that the service user receives personal care
▶ not ensuring that the service user is adequately clothed
▶ leaving the service user alone

- failing to maintain a clean and hygienic living environment
- failing to obtain necessary medical or health-care support
- not supporting social contacts
- not taking steps to provide a safe and secure environment for the service user.

In some care situations, professional carers may fail to provide some aspects of care because they have not been trained, or because they work in a setting where the emphasis is on cost saving rather than care provision. In these circumstances it becomes a form of institutional abuse. Unfortunately, there have been residential care homes and NHS trusts where service users have been found to be suffering from malnutrition as the result of such neglect. Individual workers who are deliberately neglecting service users in spite of receiving training and working in a quality caring environment are, fortunately, likely to be spotted very quickly by colleagues and supervisors.

However, carers who are supporting service users in their own homes are in different circumstances, often facing huge pressures and difficulties. Some may be reluctantly caring for a relative because they feel they have no choice; others may be barely coping with their own lives and may find caring for someone else a burden they are unable to bear. Regardless of the many possible reasons for the difficulties which can result in neglect, it is essential that a suspicion of neglect is investigated and that concerns are followed up so that help can be offered and additional support provided if necessary.

As with self-neglect, it is important that lifestyle decisions made by service users and their carers are respected, and full discussions should take place with service users and carers where there are concerns about possible neglect.

Signs and symptoms which may indicate abuse

One of the most difficult aspects of dealing with abuse is to admit that it is happening. If you are someone who has never come across deliberate abuse before, it is hard to understand and to believe that it is happening. It is not the first thing you think of when a service user has an injury or displays a change in behaviour. However, you will need to accept that abuse does happen, and is relatively common. Considering abuse should be the first option when a service user has an unexplained injury or a change in behaviour which has no obvious cause.

Abuse happens to children and adults. Victims often fail to report abuse for a range of reasons:

- they are too ill, frail or too young
- they do not have enough understanding of what is happening to them
- they are ashamed and believe that it is their own fault
- they have been threatened by the abuser or are afraid
- they do not think that they will be believed
- they do not believe that anyone has the power to stop the abuse.

Given the fact that relatively few victims report abuse without support, it is essential that those who are working in care settings are alert to the possibility of abuse and are able to recognise possible signs and symptoms. Signs and symptoms can be different in adults and children and you need to be aware of both, because regardless of the setting you work in you will come into contact with both adults and children. Your responsibilities do not end with the service user group you work with. If you believe that you have spotted signs of abuse of anyone, you have a duty to take the appropriate action.

Information on signs and symptoms comes with a warning – none of the signs or symptoms is always the result of abuse, and not all abuse produces these signs and symptoms. They are a general indicator that abuse should be considered as an explanation. You and your colleagues will need to use other skills, such as observation and communication with other professionals, in order to build up a complete picture.

Signs of possible abuse in adults

Abuse can often show as physical effects and symptoms. These are likely to be accompanied by emotional signs and changes in behaviour, but this is not always the case.

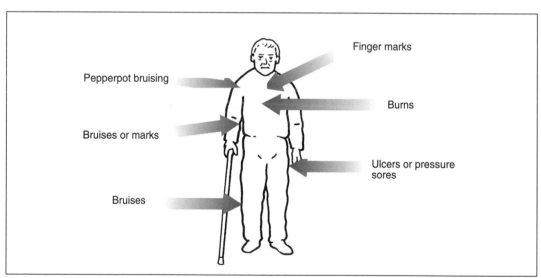

Physical signs of abuse in adults.

Any behaviour changes could indicate that the service user is a victim of some form of abuse, but remember that they are only an indicator and will need to be linked to other factors to arrive at a complete picture.

Type of sign/symptom	Description of sign/symptom	Possible form of abuse indicated
Physical	frequent or regular falls or injuries	physical
Physical	'pepperpot bruising' – small bruises, usually on the chest, caused by poking with a finger or pulling clothes tightly	physical
Physical	fingermarks – often on arms or shoulders	physical
Physical	bruising in areas not normally bruised, such as the insides of thighs and arms	physical
Physical	unusual sexual behaviour	sexual
Physical	blood or marks on underclothes	sexual
Physical	recurring genital/urinary infections	sexual
Physical	marks on wrists, upper arms or legs which could be from tying to a bed or furniture	physical/sexual
Physical	burns or scalds in unusual areas such as soles of feet, insides of thighs	physical
Physical	ulcers, bedsores or rashes caused by wet bedding/clothing	physical
Physical	missing cash or belongings, or bank accounts with unexplained withdrawals	financial
Physical	missing bank account records	financial
Emotional/behavioural	becoming withdrawn or anxious	all forms of abuse
Emotional/behavioural	loss of interest in appearance	sexual/physical/emotional
Emotional/behavioural	loss of confidence	sexual/physical/emotional
Emotional/behavioural	sudden change in attitude to financial matters	financial
Emotional/behavioural	becoming afraid of making decisions	emotional
Emotional/behavioural	sleeping problems	all forms of abuse
Emotional/behavioural	changes in eating habits	all forms of abuse

Type of sign/symptom	Description of sign/symptom	Possible form of abuse indicated
Emotional/behavioural	no longer laughing or joking	all forms of abuse
Emotional/behavioural	feeling depressed or hopeless	all forms of abuse
Emotional/behavioural	flinching or appearing afraid of close contact	physical
Emotional/behavioural	unusual sexual behaviour	sexual

Any of these behaviour changes could indicate that the service user is a victim of some form of abuse, but remember that they are only an indicator and will need to be linked to other factors to arrive at a complete picture.

Carer behaviour which should alert you to possible abuse

Sometimes, it is not the behaviour of the service user which is the first noticeable feature of an abusive situation. It can be that the first behaviour you notice is that of the carer. The following are some indications of behaviour which may give cause for concern, although with the usual warning that this is only a possible indicator of problems:

▶ reluctance to allow visitors to see the service user
▶ insistence on being present with the service user at all times
▶ derogatory or angry references to the service user
▶ excessive interest in financial accounts or assets
▶ excessive requests for repeat prescriptions.

The signs and symptoms of neglect

The effects of neglect are similar regardless of whether the neglect is at the hands of others or is self-neglect by the service user. The signs and symptoms give a clear indication that something is wrong and that the situation requires checking. It may be that the service user has made a lifestyle choice in respect of how he or she wishes to live, but this will need to be confirmed. However, it is more likely that service users are neglecting themselves or being neglected because they, or their carer, need support and assistance to ensure that they are not at risk. Any of the following may be a sign that a service user is being neglected:

▶ being dirty, unkempt or smelly
▶ wearing dirty or damaged clothing
▶ being regularly hungry
▶ living in a cold environment

- missing medical or other appointments
- having untreated illnesses or injuries
- suffering weight loss
- suffering poor skin condition, sores and rashes
- being isolated and having limited contacts.

What makes abusive situations more likely?

One of the key contributions you can make towards limiting abuse is to be aware of where abuse may be happening. It is not easy to accept that abuse is going on, and it is often simpler to find other explanations. But be prepared to *think the unthinkable*. If you know about the circumstances in which abuse has been found to occur most frequently, then you are better able to respond quickly if you suspect a problem.

It is not possible accurately to predict situations where abuse will take place – a great deal of misery could be saved if it were. It is possible, though, to identify some factors which seem to make it more likely that abuse could occur. This does not mean that abuse will definitely happen – neither should you assume that all people in these circumstances are potential abusers. But it does mean that you should be aware of the possibility when you are dealing with these situations.

Situations where child abuse can happen

Child abuse can happen in situations where:

- parents are unable to put a child's needs first
- parents or carers need to show dominance over others
- parents or carers have been poorly parented themselves
- parents or carers were abused themselves as children
- families have financial problems (this does not just mean families on low incomes)
- families have a history of poor relationships or of use of violence.

Situations where vulnerable adults may be abused at home

Adults may be abused at home in situations where:

- carers have had to change their lifestyles unwillingly
- the dependent person has communication problems, has had a personality or behaviour change (such as dementia), rejects help or is aggressive
- there is no support from family or professional carers
- carers are becoming dependent on drugs or alcohol
- carers have no privacy
- the dependent person is difficult and inconsiderate.

Check it out

Think about the service users you deal with. Make a list of how many of them fit into the circumstances outlined. Now resolve to keep a particular eye on those service users and watch for any signs that abuse may be happening. Be prepared to *think the unthinkable*.

Situations where abuse can happen in a care setting

Abuse can happen in a care setting when:

▶ staff are poorly trained or untrained
▶ there is little or no management supervision or support
▶ staff work in isolation
▶ there are inadequate numbers of staff to cope with the workload
▶ there are inadequate security arrangements
▶ there is no key worker system and good relationships are not formed between staff and residents.

Check it out

Look at your workplace. Do any of the above points apply? If any of these are the case in your workplace, you need to be aware that people can be put under so much stress that they behave abusively. Remember that abuse is not just about physical cruelty.

If none of these things happen in your workplace, then try to imagine what work would be like if they did. Sit down with a colleague, if you can, and discuss what you think the effects of any two of the items in the list would be. If you cannot do this with a colleague, you can do it on your own by making notes.

If you want to be effective in helping to stop abuse you will need to:

▶ believe that abuse happens
▶ recognise abusive behaviour
▶ be aware of when abuse can happen
▶ understand who abusers can be
▶ know the policies and procedures for handling abuse
▶ follow the individual's plan of care
▶ recognise likely abusive situations
▶ report any concerns or suspicions.

Your most important contribution will be to be *alert*. For example, an individual's plan of care or your organisational policy should specify ways in which the individual's whereabouts are constantly monitored – and if you are alert to where a vulnerable person is, and who he or she is with, you can do much to help avoid abusive situations.

There are many factors involved in building protection against abuse.

How to respond to abuse and neglect

When you find out, or suspect, that a service user is being abused or neglected, you have a responsibility to take action immediately. Concerns, suspicions and firm evidence all require an immediate response.

There are several situations in which you may find yourself in the position of having information to report concerning abuse or neglect.

▶ A service user may disclose to you that he or she is being abused or neglected.
▶ You may have clear evidence that abuse or neglect is happening.
▶ You may have concerns and suspicions, but no definite evidence.

How to respond to disclosure

The correct term for a service user telling you about abuse or neglect is 'disclosure'. If a service user discloses abuse to you, the first and most important response is that **you must believe what you are told**.

This is often harder than it sounds. If you have never been involved with an abusive situation before, it is hard to believe that such cases arise and that this could really happen.

REMEMBER

One of the biggest fears of those being abused is that no one will believe them – do not make this fear into a reality.

You must reassure the person, whether an adult or a child, that you believe what you have been told. Another common fear of people who are being abused is that it is somehow their fault – so you must also reassure them that it is not their fault and that they are in no way to blame for what has happened to them.

When a service user discloses abuse or neglect to you, try not to get into a situation where you are having to deal with a lot of detailed information. After reassuring the service user that you believe him or her, you should report the disclosure immediately to a senior colleague and hand over responsibility. This is not always possible because of the circumstances or location in which the disclosure takes place, or because the service user wants to tell you everything once he or she has started disclosing. If you do find yourself in the position of being given a great deal of information, you must be careful not to ask any leading questions – for example, do not say 'And then did he punch you?' Just ask 'And then what happened?'. Use your basic communication and listening skills so that the service user knows he or she can trust you and that you are listening. Make sure you concentrate and try to remember as much as possible so that you can record it accurately.

Another common problem which arises with disclosure is that you may be asked to keep the information secret. **You must never make this promise – it is one you cannot keep.**

What you can do is promise that you will only tell people who can help. You may well find yourself in this situation:

REMEMBER

People disclose abuse because they want it to stop. They are telling you because they want you to help make it stop. You cannot make it stop if you keep it secret.

The most important first step is to ensure that you know the procedures in your workplace for dealing with abuse and neglect. All workplaces will have policies and procedures and it is vital that you are familiar with them and know exactly who you need to report to.

Situations where you have evidence

There may be situations where you have evidence of abuse, either because you have witnessed it happening or because you have other evidence such as bank slips, forged pension books, etc. These situations must be reported immediately to your supervisor, or the person identified in the procedures followed by your workplace for cases of suspected abuse. You should make sure that you provide all the detailed evidence that you have, with full information about how you found the evidence and how and where you have recorded it.

Situations where you have concerns

It is more likely that you will not have evidence but you have noticed some of the signs or symptoms of possible abuse. You must report this as rapidly as you would if you had clear evidence.

It may be tempting to wait until you have more evidence or something happens to confirm your suspicions, but do not do this. You may not be aware of it but other people may also have concerns, and only when all the information is put together will a full picture emerge. Think of it like a jigsaw puzzle. It is not possible to see what the picture will be if you have only one or two pieces – you need to contribute your pieces so that, by working together with colleagues, as many pieces as possible can be put in place.

Dealing with abuse in a care setting

One of the most difficult situations to deal with is abuse in a professional care setting, particularly if you believe it to be taking place within your own workplace, or elsewhere in your organisation. If you are concerned about possible abuse or neglect in your workplace you should follow the same procedures as you would for any other abuse or neglect concerns.

▶ Report the problem to your line manager or supervisor.
▶ If you suspect that your manager is involved, or will not take action, you must refer it to a more senior manager who is likely to be impartial.
▶ If you do not feel confident that you can report the abuse to anyone within

your workplace or organisation, you should report your concerns to the National Care Standards Commission, which is responsible for ensuring that standards are maintained in all care settings.

Whistle-blowing

Reporting concerns about practice in your workplace is known as 'whistle-blowing' and you cannot be victimised for doing this. An Act of Parliament protects you – it is called the UK Public Interest Disclosure Act. The Act came into force on 2 July 1999. It encourages people to 'blow the whistle' about malpractice in the workplace and is designed to ensure that organisations respond by acting on the message rather than punishing the messenger.

The Act applies to employees reporting crime, civil offences (including negligence, breach of contract, etc.), miscarriage of justice, danger to health and safety or the environment, and the covering up of any of these. It applies whether or not the information is confidential, and extends to malpractice occurring in the UK and any other country or territory.

In addition to employees, it covers trainees, agency staff, contractors, home workers and every professional in the NHS. The Act means that your employer cannot take any action to victimise you because you have reported genuine concerns.

Recording

Any information you have, whether it is simply concerns, hard evidence, or a disclosure, must be carefully recorded. You should write down your evidence, or if you are unable to do so for any reason, you should record it on audio tape. It is not acceptable to pass on your concerns verbally without backing this up with a recorded report. Verbal information can be altered and can have its meaning changed very easily when it is passed on. Think about the children's game of Chinese Whispers – by the time the whispered phrase reaches the end of it journey, it is usually changed beyond all recognition.

Your record should be detailed and clear, and should include information about:

▶ everything you observed
▶ anything you have been told – but make sure that it is clear that this is not something you have seen for yourself
▶ any previous concerns you may have had
▶ what has raised your concerns on this occasion.

> P. was visited by her son this afternoon. She was very quiet over tea, did not join in conversation or joke with anyone. Just said she was tired when asked what was wrong. Went to her room without going into lounge for the 'seconds evening'. Said she thought the clothes were too expensive and she couldn't afford them. Unusual for her. Similar to incident about a month ago when she said she couldn't afford the hairdresser - again after a visit from her son.
> Needs to be watched. Is he getting money from her? For discussion at planning meeting.

Check it out

Write a report on concerns about an abuse situation which could occur in your workplace. If you are aware of abuse situations which have happened, you could report on one of them, making sure you do not use service users' names or any other information which could identify them. If not, make up the details. State to whom, in your workplace, you would give the report.

The effects of abuse

Abuse devastates those who suffer it. It causes people to lose their self-esteem and their confidence. Many adults and children become withdrawn and difficult to communicate with. Anger is a common emotion among people who have been abused. It may be directed against the abuser, or at those people around them who failed to recognise the abuse and stop it happening.

One of the greatest tragedies is when people who have been abused turn their anger against themselves and blame themselves for everything that has happened to them. These are situations which require expert help, and this should be available to anyone who has been abused, regardless of the circumstances.

In an earlier section of this outcome you learned about the signs and symptoms of abuse. Some of the behaviour changes which can be signs of abuse can become permanent, or certainly very long-lasting. There are very few survivors of abuse whose personality remains unchanged, and for those who do conquer the effects of abuse, it is a long, hard fight.

The abuser, often called the 'perpetrator', also requires expert help, and this should be available through various agencies depending on the type and seriousness of the abuse. People who abuse, whether their victims are children or vulnerable adults, receive very little sympathy or understanding from society. There is no public recognition that some abusers may have been under tremendous strain and pressure, and abusers may find that they have no support from friends or family. Many abusers will face the consequences of their actions alone.

DID YOU KNOW?

Prisoners who are serving sentences for child abuse, or for abuse of vulnerable adults, have to be kept in separate areas of the prison for their own safety. If they were allowed to mix with other prisoners, they could be seriously assaulted or even killed.

Care workers who have to deal with abusive situations will have different emotional reactions. There is no 'right way' to react. Everyone is different and will deal with things in his or her own way. If you have to deal with abuse, these are some of the ways you may feel, and some steps you can take which may help.

Shock

You may feel quite traumatised by the abusive incident. It is normal to find that you cannot get the incident off your mind, that you have difficulty concentrating on other things, or that you keep having 'flashbacks' and re-enact the situation in your head. You may also feel that you need to keep talking about what happened.

Talking can be very beneficial, but if you are discussing an incident outside your workplace, you must remember rules of confidentiality and *never* use names. You will find that you can talk about the circumstances just as well by referring to 'the boy' or 'the father' or 'the daughter'. This way of talking does become second nature, and is useful because it allows you to share your feelings about things which have happened at work while maintaining confidentiality.

These feelings are likely to last for a fairly short time, and are a natural reaction to shock and trauma. If at any time you feel that you are having difficulty, you must talk to your manager or supervisor, who should be able to help.

Anger

Alternatively, the situation may have made you feel very angry, and you may have an overwhelming urge to inflict some damage on the perpetrator of the abuse. While this is understandable, it is not professional and you will have to find other ways of dealing with your anger. Again, your supervisor or manager should help you to work through your feelings.

Everyone has different ways of dealing with anger, such as taking physical exercise, doing housework, punching a cushion, writing feelings down and then tearing up the paper, crying or telling your best friend. Whatever you do with your anger in ordinary situations, you should do the same in this situation (just remember to respect confidentiality if you need to tell your best friend – miss out the names). It is perfectly legitimate to be angry, but you cannot bring this anger into the professional relationship.

Distress

The situation may have made you distressed, and you may want to go home and have a good cry, or give your own relatives an extra hug. This is a perfectly normal reaction. No matter how many years you work, or how many times it happens, you may still feel the same way.

Some workplaces will have arrangements in place where workers are able to share difficult situations and get support from each other. Others may not have any formal meetings or groups arranged, but colleagues will offer each other support and advice in an informal way. You may find that work colleagues who have had similar experiences are the best people with whom to share your feelings.

There is, of course, the possibility that the situation may have brought back painful memories for you of abuse you have suffered in your own past. This is often the most difficult situation to deal with, because you may feel as if you should be able to help because you know how it feels to be abused, but your own experience has left you without any room to deal with the feelings of others. There are many avenues of support now available to survivors of abuse. You can find out about the nearest support confidentially, if you do not want your workplace colleagues or supervisor to know.

There is no doubt that dealing with abuse is one of the most stressful aspects of working in care. There is nothing odd or abnormal about feeling that you need to share what you have experienced and looking for support from others. This is a perfectly reasonable reaction and, in fact, most experienced managers would be far more concerned about a worker involved in dealing with abuse who appears quite unaffected by it, than about one who comes looking for guidance and reassurance.

REMEMBER

▶ Feeling upset is normal.
▶ Talk about the incident if that helps, but respect the rules of confidentiality and miss out the names.
▶ Being angry is OK, but deal with it sensibly – take physical exercise, do the housework, cry.
▶ Do not be unprofessional with the abuser.
▶ If you are a survivor of abuse and you find it hard to deal with, ask for help.

How the law affects what you do

Much of the work in caring is governed by legislation, but the only group where legislation specifically provides for protection from abuse is children. Older people, people with a learning disability, physical disabilities or mental health problems have service provision, restrictions, rights and all sorts of other requirements laid down in law, but no overall legal framework to provide protection from abuse. The laws which cover your work in the field of care are summarised in the table on the next page.

Service user group	Laws which govern their care	Protection from abuse?
Children	Children Act 1989	Yes
People with mental health problems	Mental Health Act 1983	No
Adults with a learning disability	Mental Health Act 1983	No
Adults with disabilities	Chronically Sick and Disabled Persons Act 1986 Disability Discrimination Act 1995	No
Older people	National Assistance Act 1948 NHS and Community Care Act 1990	No
All service user groups	Care Standards Act 2000	Yes, through raising standards

There are, however a number of sets of guidelines, policies and procedures in respect of abuse for service user groups other than children, and you will need to ensure that you are familiar with policies for your area of work and particularly with those policies which apply in your own workplace.

Check it out

Ask your supervisor if there are any laws or guidelines which govern the procedures in your workplace for dealing with abuse. There should be a written policy and guidelines to be followed if abuse is suspected. Ask if there are any laws or guidelines which are related to the way you work. Check with experienced colleagues about situations they have dealt with and ask them to tell you about what happened.

Recent policy approaches to protecting children and vulnerable adults have concentrated on improving and monitoring the quality of the service provided to them. The principle behind this is that if the overall quality of practice in care is constantly improved, then well-trained staff working to high standards are less likely to abuse service users, and are more likely to identify and deal effectively with any abuse they find.

Government policies and guidelines

The most important set of government guidelines on child protection is called 'Working Together to Safeguard Children'. It lays down practices for co-operation between agencies. Published in 1999, it forms the basis for present child protection work. The guidelines ensure that information is shared between agencies and professionals, and that decisions in respect of children are not taken by just one person.

A similar set of guidelines was published by the government about adults, called 'No Secrets' (see page 57). These guidelines state that older people have specific rights, which include being treated with respect, and being able to live in their home and community without fear of physical or emotional violence or harassment.

The guidance gives local authorities the lead responsibility in co-ordinating the procedures. Each local authority area must have a multi-agency management committee for the protection of vulnerable adults, which will develop policies, protocols and practices. The guidance covers:

▶ identification of those at risk
▶ setting up an inter-agency framework
▶ developing inter-agency procedures for responding in individual cases
▶ recruitment, training and other staff and management issues.

A government White Paper published in 2001, 'Valuing People: A New Strategy for Learning Disability in the 21st Century', sets out the ways in which services for people with a learning disability will be improved. 'Valuing People' sets out four main principles for service provision for people with a learning disability:

▶ civil rights
▶ independence
▶ choice
▶ inclusion.

The White Paper also makes it clear that people with a learning disability are entitled to the full protection of the law.

Vulnerable adults are entitled to respect and the full protection of the law.

What does the law say about protecting children?

The Children Act 1989 requires that local authority social services departments provide protection from abuse for children in their area. The Act of Parliament gives powers to social services departments, following the procedures laid down by the Area Child Protection Committee, to take legal steps to ensure the safety of children.

The government produced a Green Paper called 'Every Child Matters' in late 2003. Among other changes, this paper proposes that co-operation between agencies is no longer sufficient to protect children, and that local authorities must appoint a Director for Children's Services, to replace the present directors of social services and of education. It is hoped that bringing the two departments together in this way will improve the services for children, and encourage better communication and ways of working together.

What happens in an emergency?

In an emergency, at the moment, a social worker or an NSPCC officer can apply to a magistrate for an order to look after a child. This is an Emergency Protection Order (known as an EPO). The police are also able to take immediate steps to protect children in an emergency situation. This is a Police Protection Order, or PPO. These orders require evidence which shows that there is reasonable cause to believe that a child may suffer 'significant harm'. They are short-term orders, usually for 3-7 days, and are followed by a court hearing where more detailed evidence is produced and the parents are represented.

The three agencies able to take legal steps to protect children.

Not all investigations into abuse are emergencies, and not all involve legal proceedings. Some abusive, or potentially abusive, situations are dealt with by working with the family, usually by agreeing a 'contract' between social services and the family.

What does the law say about protecting vulnerable adults?

The Acts of Parliament which are mainly concerned with provisions for vulnerable adults are the National Assistance Act 1948 and the NHS and Community Care Act 1990. They do not specifically give social services departments a 'duty to protect' but, of course, people are protected by the law. If a vulnerable adult is abused and that abuse is considered to be a criminal offence, then the police will act. It is sometimes thought that if the victim is confused, a prosecution will not be brought – this is not so. All vulnerable adults will have the full protection of the law if any criminal offences are committed.

Some vulnerable adults suffer abuse in residential or hospital settings. These settings are controlled by legislation. Hospitals have complaints procedures and arrangements for allowing 'whistle-blowers' who have concerns about abuse to come forward. Residential homes and nursing homes have to be registered with the National Care Standards Commissioner, who will investigate allegations of abuse and can ultimately close an unsatisfactory residential home or nursing home.

The Mental Health Act 1983 (and the draft Mental Health Bill) forms the framework for service provision for people with mental health problems and people with a learning disability. There are provisions within this legislation for social services departments to assume responsibility for people who are so 'mentally impaired' that they are not able to be responsible for their own affairs. This is called **guardianship**. However, like all other vulnerable adults, there is no specific duty to protect people from abuse.

The government White Paper published in 2001, 'Valuing People' (see page 77) will form the basis for services to all people with a learning disability and will provide rights, but no specific duty of protection.

The Chronically Sick and Disabled Persons Act and the Disability Discrimination Act provide disabled people with rights, services and protection from discrimination, but they do not provide any means of comprehensive protection from abuse.

As with all vulnerable groups, there is a long and tragic history to the physical and emotional abuse suffered by people with physical disabilities or a learning disability. Public humiliation and abuse of those with mental health problems is still visible today, so it is hardly surprising that abuse on an individual level is still all too commonplace.

What happens in an emergency?

Many social services departments now have procedures in place similar to those for protecting children. There will be an investigation of the alleged or suspected abuse, followed by a case conference where information will be shared between all the professionals concerned and a plan of action will be worked out. The vulnerable adult concerned and/or a friend or advocate will also be invited to take part in the conference if he or she wishes.

What if a professional carer abuses?

There are special procedures in place for investigating abuse which is inflicted by care workers or foster carers. It is investigated by an outside agency and immediate steps are taken to remove the suspected abuser (often called the 'perpetrator') from contact until the investigation has been completed.

Outcome activity 1.4

You can complete this activity by yourself, or in a group. The task is to produce an information pack which can be used by all members of staff who have to deal with a situation involving abuse. You should assume that all staff will have access to a computer, so if you prefer, you can produce an on-line information pack.

Step 1

Make a list of all the different forms of abuse and neglect. Include a brief explanation of each form you identify.

Step 2

Make a list of the kinds of behaviour changes which may indicate that abuse has taken place. Show which type of abuse may be indicated by the behaviour changes.

Step 3

Describe the policies and procedures of the organisation you work for which are designed to protect service users from abuse. Make notes about how these fit in with legal requirements.

Step 4

Research national and local sources of support for people who have been abused. Include in your pack information about the services offered, who can use them, contact points, addresses, websites and details of the type of support which can be provided.

Behaviour which is unacceptable

All abusive behaviour is unacceptable. However, you may come across other kinds of behaviour which you may not be able to define directly as abusive, but which are close to it – or could lead to an abusive situation if not dealt with.

Generally, you can define behaviour as unacceptable if:

▶ it is outside what you would normally see in that situation
▶ it does not take into account the needs or views of others
▶ people are afraid or intimidated
▶ people are undermined or made to feel guilty
▶ the behaviour is likely to cause distress or unhappiness to others.

Examples of unacceptable behaviour include:

▶ threatening violence
▶ subjecting someone to unwelcome sexual attention
▶ shouting or playing loud music in a quiet area, or late at night
▶ verbal abuse, racist or sexist taunts
▶ spreading malicious gossip about someone
▶ attempting to isolate someone.

All of these types of behaviour are oppressive to others and need to be challenged. You can probably think of many other situations in your own workplace which have caused unhappiness. You may have had to deal with difficult situations, or have seen others deal with them, or perhaps you have wished that you had done something to challenge unacceptable behaviour.

Unacceptable behaviour from colleagues

You may come across unacceptable and oppressive behaviour in your colleagues or other professionals in your workplace. Behaviour which is abusive is dealt with in the previous outcome. But you may see or hear a colleague behaving in a way which, while it is not abusive as such, may be oppressive and unacceptable. This can take various forms, such as:

▶ speaking about service users in a derogatory way
▶ speaking to service users in a rude or dismissive way
▶ humiliating service users
▶ undermining people's self-esteem and confidence
▶ bullying or intimidation
▶ patronising and talking down to people
▶ removing people's right to exercise choice
▶ failing to recognise and treat people as individuals
▶ not respecting people's culture, values and beliefs.

In short, the types of behaviour which are unacceptable from workers in care settings are those which simply fail to meet the standards required of good quality practitioners. Any care worker who fails to remember that all people are individuals and all have a right to be valued and accepted is likely to fall into oppressive or inappropriate behaviour.

Check it out

Ask three colleagues in your workplace to state one behaviour that they would find unacceptable in (a) a service user and (b) a colleague. Compare the six answers and see if they have anything in common. Find out from your supervisor about the type of behaviour that is challenged in your workplace, and that which is allowed.

How to challenge unacceptable behaviour

Steps in dealing with difficult situations

Step 1 Consider all the people involved in the situation

If you have some knowledge of an individual's background, culture and beliefs, it may be easier to see why he or she is behaving in a particular way. This does not make it acceptable, just easier to understand. For example, an individual who has been in a position of wealth or power may be used to giving people instructions and expecting to have immediate attention, and may be quite rude if it does not happen. People may also become aggressive or disruptive because they:

▶ are frustrated about having to submit to rules of behaviour, and feel their choices are restricted
▶ feel they have been ignored, insulted or their rights have been denied
▶ are suffering ill-health, or the side-effects of medication
▶ have learned in the past that this behaviour will gain them attention or other benefits
▶ have taken alcohol or illicit drugs.

None of these reasons means that aggression is going to be tolerated, but approaching the situation with some understanding allows people to maintain their dignity while adapting their behaviour.

Step 2 Be aware of everyone's needs

If you are in a work situation, it can be complicated by the fact that the person whose oppressive behaviour you are challenging may also be one of your service users. In this case, it is important to ensure that you challenge the behaviour without becoming aggressive or intimidating yourself, and that you do not undermine the individual.

Step 3 Decide on the best approach

How you decide to deal with an incident of unacceptable behaviour will depend on:

▶ whether the behaviour is violent or non-violent – if the behaviour is violent, what the potential dangers of the situation are, who may be in danger, and what needs to be done to help those in danger
▶ who is involved, and how well you know them and know how to deal with them
▶ whether you need help, and who is available to help you
▶ whether the cause is obvious and the solution is easy to find.

Clearly, you will need to weigh up the situation quickly, in order to deal with it promptly. You will, no doubt, feel under pressure, as this is a stressful situation to be in, whether you are experienced or not. Try to remain calm and think clearly.

Step 4 Deal with non-violent behaviour

If the behaviour you have to deal with is not physical aggression or violence, then you will need to ensure that you challenge it in a situation which provides privacy and dignity. You should challenge without becoming aggressive; remain calm and quietly state what you consider to be unacceptable about the behaviour. Do not try to approach the subject from various angles, or drop hints. Be clear about the problem and what you want to happen.

For example: 'Bill, you have been playing your radio very loudly until quite late each night. Other residents are finding it difficult to get to sleep. I would like you to stop playing it so loudly if you want to have it on late.' You may well have to negotiate with Bill about times, and the provision of headphones, but do not be drawn into an argument and do not be sidetracked into irrelevant discussions. Keep to the point:

Bill: 'Who's been complaining? No one's complained to me. Who is it?'

You: 'Bill, this is about your radio being too loud. The issue is not about who complained, but about the fact that it is upsetting residents and I want you to stop doing it.'

By the end of this discussion, Bill should be very clear about what is being required of him and be in no doubt that his behaviour will have to change.

Step 5 Attempt to calm a potentially violent situation

It is always better to avoid a violent situation than to respond to one, so you need to be aware of the signals which may indicate that violence could erupt. Be on the lookout for verbal aggression; raised volume and pitch of voice; threatening and aggressive gestures; pacing up and down; quick, darting eye movements; prolonged eye contact.

Try to respond in ways least likely to provoke further aggression.

- Use listening skills, and appear confident (but not cocky).
- Keep your voice calm and at a level pitch.
- Do not argue.
- Do not get drawn into prolonged eye contact.
- Attempt to defuse the situation with empathy and understanding. For example: 'I realise you must be upset if you believe that George said that about you. I can see that you're very angry. Tell me about what happened.'

Be prepared to try a different approach if you find you are not getting anywhere. Always make sure that an aggressor has a way out with dignity, both physically and emotionally.

DID YOU KNOW?

There is a technique which is recommended for use in situations which become violent. It is called 'Breakaway' and is approved by the Home Office for use in all types of care settings. It provides you with methods for dealing with a physical threat or attack without causing injury. Ask your employer to arrange for you to attend a course with an approved trainer.

Step 6 Deal with aggressive or violent behaviour

Be aware of the situation you are in and take some common-sense precautions: make sure that you know where the exits are, and move so that the aggressor is not between you and the exit; notice if there is anything which could be used as a weapon, and try to move away from it; make sure that the aggressor has enough personal space, and do not crowd him or her.

If you are faced with a violent situation, you should try to remain calm (even though that is easier said than done!) and not resort to violence or aggression yourself.

It is often the case that a simple technique like holding up a hand in front of you, as if you were directing traffic, and shouting 'Stop' may deflect an attacker, or stop him or her long enough for you to get away. You should remove yourself from the situation as speedily as possible.

If there are other, vulnerable people at risk, you must decide whether you can summon help more effectively from outside or inside the situation.

If you decide to remain, you must summon help at once. You should do one of the following.

- Press a panic alarm or buzzer, if one is provided.
- Shout 'help!' very loudly and continuously.

- Send someone for help.
- Call the police, or security, or shout for someone else to do so.

Do not try to be a hero – that is not your job.

Check it out

Your workplace should have a policy on dealing with aggression and violence. Ask to see it and make sure that you read it carefully.

REMEMBER

- Everyone is different and will react differently to each situation.
- You are the factor that makes the difference.
- Learn to know yourself before you think you can know about others.
- Each person should be valued as a unique individual.

Reasons for challenging behaviour

All of us become distressed at some time and the causes of that distress are varied and differ from individual to individual. What distresses one person will not distress another; a situation which reduces one person to a fit of sobbing will be shrugged off by another. Be careful that you do not confuse the causes of distress with the reasons for distress. Causes can be a range of external factors, but reasons are much deeper, psychological influences which affect the way different people respond in different circumstances.

All of us have a broadly similar process of emotional development, but as each person is an individual who has grown and developed in different circumstances, it is inevitable that the overall effects will be different for each person. However, psychologists have identified some basic forms of behaviour which can be broadly applied to explain why people behave in the way they do.

Nature or nurture

There has always been much debate in the psychological world about whether our emotional responses are inborn (we have them by nature) or whether they are learned from our environment (nurture). The most likely explanation is that they are a combination of the two. Most psychologists agree that there is an inborn response – evidence from work with very young babies shows how they respond to sounds, pain and loss of support. As we grow and develop we learn to respond to other different stimuli, in different ways. It is important to recognise that although these may be the basic stimuli which humans respond to, what you have to deal with when working in care is *how* humans respond – in other words, what people do in response to a distressing situation.

The crying response is the earliest human response. This is extremely useful for babies because it alerts the mother to the baby's needs – it is the way the baby attracts its mother's attention in order to have its needs met. Thus crying is an effective appeal for help – and many people continue this into adulthood.

Babies appear to demonstrate three different emotional responses: fear, rage and love. These are recognised as the basic building blocks on which the range of complex human emotions are subsequently built. It is possible to identify these three major components in the emotions experienced by older children, adolescents, and adults. As people gain more experience of life and are exposed to a wider range of influences, the emotions become complex and more difficult to deal with.

Crying alerts a mother to her baby's needs.

Your role is not that of a psychologist or a psychiatrist, but it is important that you are aware of the way in which human beings develop emotionally and that you have a broad understanding of how the complex emotions that you are likely to deal with in your work setting have come about.

DID YOU KNOW?

Psychologists and psychiatrists dealing with people suffering from mental health problems or disturbed emotional behaviour can identify the three basic emotional responses of rage, fear and love plus a fourth category of depression, which has never been identified in babies. One view connects emotional responses with the 'direction' of behaviour. Much of human behaviour can be said to have a clear direction either towards, away from, against or inwards. Rage is directed against the cause of the frustration, fear causes people to move away from the object of their fear, love draws people towards the object of their affection and depression turns all behaviour inwards against oneself.

Physical effects of strong emotions

Definite and measurable physical effects are caused by powerful emotional responses. It is useful to be aware of these effects as they can often be an early indicator of a potentially highly charged or dangerous situation. The physical effect of strong emotion can be:

▶ pupils dilate, the eyelids open wider than usual, and the eyes protrude
▶ speed and strength of heart beat are increased
▶ blood pressure is increased and blood is forced outwards towards the surface of the body – this is clearly noticeable in flushing of the face and neck
▶ the hair can stand up, causing goose pimples

- breathing patterns will change – they can be either faster or slower
- lung function alters to allow up to 25 per cent more oxygen to be absorbed
- more sweat is produced – this can often be identified as a 'cold sweat'
- the salivary glands are inhibited – the mouth feels dry
- the digestive system is affected – the gastric fluids are reduced and blood is withdrawn from the digestive organs
- adrenaline flow is increased, which reinforces all the above effects and increases blood clotting.

Fight or flight

This reaction to strong emotions is said to prepare humans for 'fight or flight'. This is a basic human response to a situation in which we are placed under threat – the body prepares us either to fight or to run away.

There are other very noticeable effects of a highly emotional state. People will often have what appears to be increased energy – they don't speak, they shout, and they don't sit or stand still, they will run or walk about, slam doors and possibly throw things. The additional energy and strength generated by powerful emotions can be extremely valuable and can even help to preserve life. There are many stories about people performing heroic feats of strength or endurance when in the most dangerous situations, for example in a house fire or an accident. Another apparent effect of strong emotional responses is a temporary lessening of the awareness of pain. People can act regardless of severe injury, for example on the battlefield or in an accident or other emergency, and it is only when the immediate threat has passed that they become aware of their injuries.

Controlling emotions

As we grow and develop, most of us learn to control these powerful emotions. The process of growing up socialises us into behaving in a way which is viewed as acceptable in society.

Check it out

Think about how you deal with your own powerful emotions. Think of occasions when

a) you have felt strong emotions but managed to keep them under control and not show your distress publicly

b) you have experienced powerful emotions which you have shown publicly.

Try to identify the difference in circumstances and the factors which caused the two different responses.

Most people most of the time behave within the accepted norms of society.

However, on occasions the emotions may become too powerful or the normal control is relaxed, resulting in a display of emotion which is recognised as distress. People can become distressed for a wide range of causes, and these can be the trigger for an underlying emotional response. There are some common causes of distress, and it is helpful for you to be aware of situations and circumstances which can act as triggers. People commonly become distressed when:

▶ they are informed of the death or serious illness of someone close to them
▶ they receive bad or worrying news
▶ there are problems with a relationship which is important to them
▶ they become stressed through an overload of work or family pressures
▶ they have serious worries such as debt, problems at work, or problems with the family
▶ they are reacting to the behaviour of others towards them
▶ they are responding to something that they have heard, seen or read in the media
▶ they are in an environment which they find frustrating or restricting
▶ they are in an environment which they find intensely irritating, for example it is noisy or they are unable to find any personal space
▶ they are deprived of information and are fearful
▶ they have full information about a situation and they remain fearful of it
▶ they are anxious about a forthcoming event
▶ they are unable to achieve the objectives they have set themselves.

Everyone has a breaking point.

Check it out

Identify six potential triggers for distress which relate to your own work setting.

Signs that distress is leading to aggressive behaviour

When you have a working knowledge of a service user's behaviour over a period of time it becomes easy to identify when he or she is becoming distressed. You will find that you can recognise small signs that indicate a change in mood. However, you will not always be in a situation of knowing your service users well and in fact you may have to deal with distress in a carer or even a work colleague. There are some general indications that an individual is becoming distressed which you can use in order to take immediate action. You are most likely to notice:

▶ changes in the voice – it may be raised or at a higher pitch than usual
▶ changes in facial expression – this could be scowling, crying or snarling
▶ changes in eyes – pupils could be dilated and eyes open wider
▶ body language could demonstrate agitation, or people may adopt an aggressive stance, leaning forward with fists clenched
▶ the face and neck are likely to be reddened
▶ there may be sweating
▶ breathing patterns may change, and may become faster than normal.

A distressed and frustrated service user can develop into an aggressive service user in some circumstances. If you feel that someone is becoming aggressive and potentially violent, for example if he or she starts shouting or throwing things, you should immediately summon help.

Anger is not always directed at others – it can be turned inwards against the individual. You may be faced with the situation where distressed, hurt and angry individuals make it clear to you that they intend to harm themselves. You have a responsibility to take immediate action in order to protect the individual in such cases. It is also essential that you advise the individual that you will have to take steps to attempt to prevent any self-harm. It is never acceptable for you to allow people to harm themselves.

Use of physical restraint

Physically restraining service users is very much a last resort and restraint should be used only if it is absolutely unavoidable. Every workplace has a policy on the use of physical restraint, and you will need to be sure that you know what it is for your own setting. The policies vary, but are likely to include the following principles.

▶ Before using restraint, staff should have good grounds for believing that immediate action is necessary to prevent a service user from significantly injuring himself/herself or others, or causing serious damage to property.

- Staff should take steps in advance to avoid the need for physical restraint, such as by discussing or providing diversion from the problem; and the service user should be warned that physical restraint will be used unless he or she stops.
- Only the minimum force necessary to prevent injury or damage should be used.
- Every effort should be made to have other staff present before applying restraint. These staff can act both as assistants and witnesses.
- As soon as it is safe, restraint should be gradually relaxed to allow the service user to regain self-control.
- Restraint must be an act of care and control, not punishment.
- Physical restraint must never be used purely to force service users to comply with staff instructions when there is no immediate risk to people or property.

These are the general principles, but you must also act within the law. Excessive use of physical restraint can be viewed as assault, and result in a criminal charge. This is why it is essential that you follow your workplace policy, and discuss with your supervisor exactly what steps you must take. All workplaces are likely to provide training in the use of physical restraint and methods of managing aggression, so make sure that you take up any opportunity to receive training.

Being involved in an incident of violence or aggression can be very distressing and you should ask for support from your supervisor if you find that you are affected by an incident you have witnessed or been involved in.

Recording an incident

It is also important that you write a report of the incident as soon as possible. You may think that you will never forget what you saw or heard, but details do become blurred with time and repetition. Your workplace may have a special form or you may have to write a report. If there is a reason why writing a report is not possible, then you should record your evidence on audio tape. It is not acceptable to pass on the information verbally – there must be a record which can be referred to. Your evidence may be needed by the social workers and police officers who will investigate the situation. It may be useful for a doctor who will conduct an examination, or it may be needed for the case conference or for court proceedings.

How dealing with distress or aggression can affect you

Do not underestimate how upsetting it can be to deal with somebody who is displaying powerful emotions. Feeling concerned, upset or even angry after a particularly difficult experience with a service user is perfectly normal. The fact that you continue to have an emotional response after a situation is over is in no way a reflection on the quality of your work or your ability as a care worker. After dealing with any difficult or emotional situation most people are likely to continue to think about it for some time. One of the best ways to deal with this is to discuss it with your line manager or supervisor; or you could talk to a close friend or relative, always ensuring that you never compromise a service user's right to confidentiality. If you find after a period of time that you are unable to put a particular incident out of your mind or you feel that it is interfering with your work, there are other sources of help available to you, both within your workplace and outside it. Talk to your line manager or supervisor to ensure that you have access to any help you need.

The distress of others, whether it takes the form of anger or sadness or anxiety, will always be distressing for the person who works with them. But if you are able to develop your skills and knowledge so that you can identify distress, contribute towards reducing it and offer effective help and support to those who are experiencing it, then you are making a useful and meaningful contribution to the provision of quality care.

Outcome activity 1.5

In this activity, you will show your knowledge about the ways in which aggression can be dealt with. You can either work alone and write a short story, or work in a group and develop a role play which you then perform. Regardless of which approach you choose, the steps to follow are similar.

Step 1
Think of a situation involving aggression which could take place in any care setting. The situation must involve at least one service user and one staff member; other service users and staff members can be involved as observers or in providing support. The scenario should show how the aggressive behaviour developed, and its main cause. You should also show in detail how the situation built up and how it became clear that the service user was becoming aggressive. Your story or role play must describe how the staff member dealt with the episode, and the results. Do not forget to include information about the effects of the incident on service users and staff who were not directly involved.

Step 2
If you are working alone, word process your short story; if you are in a group, work together to plan the presentation of your role play. Make sure that everyone playing a role understands the feelings of the person he or she is portraying.

Step 3
If you have written a short story, present it to your group, either by reading it aloud or by printing and circulating copies. Lead a discussion about how the main characters in your story felt, and why they reacted in the way they did.

If you have prepared a role play, present it to your group and then hold a discussion, with each participant describing in full the feelings of the person he or she played.

Step 4
Lead your discussion to a conclusion about how effective the approach to the aggressive situation was, and the likely outcomes of different approaches.

Communication is all about the way people reach out to one another. It is an essential part of all relationships, and the ability to communicate well with service users, colleagues and others is a basic requirement for doing your job.

Communication is not just talking – we use touch, facial expressions and body movements when we are communicating with people personally, and there are many means of written and electronic communication in today's society.

It is important that you learn to communicate well even where there are differences in individuals' abilities and methods of communication which can cause problems. This unit is about the many ways in which you can make communication more effective in any context.

Outcome 1: Apply the principles of effective communication with individuals

Giving and receiving accurate information is vitally important for any care setting. The information could be about an individual who is being cared for in your workplace, a relative or friend, or it could be about the organisation itself, about or for somebody who works there, or for administrative purposes. The information could come to you in a range of ways:

- verbally, for example in a conversation either face-to-face or on the telephone
- on paper, for example in a letter, a service user's health record or instructions from a health professional
- electronically, by fax or on a computer.

Whatever the purpose of the information, it is important that you record it accurately. It is also important that you pass on any information correctly, in the right form and to the right person. Recording information is essential in health and care services, because the services that are provided are about *people* rather than objects, so it is vital that information is accurate, accessible and readable.

Ways of receiving and passing on information

Today within health and care there are many ways in which information is circulated between agencies, colleagues, other team members, individuals receiving care, carers, volunteers and so on. The growth of electronic communication has meant a considerable change in the way that people receive and send information, in comparison to only a few years ago when information sharing was limited to face-to-face meetings, telephone calls or posted letters.

Telephone

One of the commonest means of communication is the telephone. It has advantages because it is instant, straightforward and is a relatively safe and accurate way of communicating and passing on information. However, there are some disadvantages to the telephone in that it can often be difficult to ensure that you have clearly understood what has been said. There can be problems with telephone lines which cause crackling and technical difficulties. It is also possible to misinterpret somebody's meaning when you cannot pick up other signals, such as facial expression and body language. If you regularly take or place messages on the telephone, there are some very simple steps that you can take to ensure that you cut down the risk of getting a message wrong.

▶ Make sure that you check the name of the person who is calling. If necessary, ask the person to spell his or her name and be sure that you have it right. Repeat it to make sure. It is easy to mix up Thomas and Thompson, Williams and Wilkins, and so on. You may also need to take the person's address, and again it is worthwhile asking him or her to spell the details to ensure that you have written them correctly.

Always ask for a return telephone number so that the person who receives the message can phone back if necessary. There is nothing more infuriating than receiving a message on which you have some queries and no means of contacting the person who has left it for you. You should read back the message itself to the person who is leaving it just to check that you have the correct information and that you have understood his or her meaning.

Incoming post

If it is part of your role to open and check any incoming post, you must make sure that you:

▶ open it as soon as it arrives
▶ follow your own workplace procedures for dealing with incoming mail – this is likely to involve stamping it with the date it is received
▶ pass it on to the appropriate person for it to be dealt with or filed. See page 101 for advice on how to deal with confidential information.

Faxed information

The steps for dealing with an incoming fax message are as follows.

▶ Take the fax from the machine.

- ▶ Read the cover sheet – this will tell you who the fax is for, who it is from (it should include telephone and fax numbers) and how many pages there should be.
- ▶ Check that the correct number of pages have been received. If a fax has misprinted or has pages missing, contact the telephone number identified on the cover sheet and ask for the information to be sent again. If there is no telephone number, send a fax immediately to the sending fax number asking for the fax to be resent.
- ▶ Follow your organisation's procedure for dealing with incoming faxes. Make sure the fax is handed to the appropriate person as soon as possible.

See page 102 for information about dealing with confidential information which comes in by fax.

E-mail

E-mail is a very frequently used means of communication within and between workplaces. It is fast, convenient and easy to use for many people. Large reports and complex information which would be cumbersome to post or fax can be transmitted as an attachment to an e-mail in seconds. However, not everyone in all workplaces has access to e-mail and not all electronic transmission is secure. Be aware of this if you are sending highly sensitive and confidential material. If you do send and receive information by e-mail you should:

E-mail is a fast and efficient method of communication in most circumstances.

- ▶ follow the guidelines in your workplace for using e-mail and the transmission of confidential material
- ▶ open all your e-mails and respond to them promptly
- ▶ save any confidential messages or attachments in an appropriate, password-protected file or folder, and delete them from your inbox unless that is also protected
- ▶ return promptly any e-mails you have received in error
- ▶ not give your password to anyone.

Outgoing mail

If you have to write information to send to another organisation, whether it is by letter or by fax or e-mail, you should be sure that the contents are clear, cannot be misunderstood and are to the point. Do not write a rambling, long letter which obliges recipients to hunt for the information they need.

It is likely that, within many organisations, you will need to show any faxes or letters to your supervisor or manager before they leave the premises. This safeguard is in place in many workplaces for the good reason that information being sent on behalf of your employer must be accurate and appropriate. As your employer is the person ultimately responsible for any information sent out, he or she will want to have procedures in place to check this.

Confidentiality

The single most important requirement for anyone who works in a care setting is to be trustworthy. It is no use having the kindest doctor in the world if you discover that she has been chatting to your next door neighbour about how bad your haemorrhoids are! You will have to make confidentiality part of your life.

Confidentiality means not giving any information to anyone unless there is a reason to do so. This sounds very straightforward, and in theory it is, but you need to know what this means in practice.

DID YOU KNOW?

Everyone has one friend to whom they can talk in absolute confidence! The problem is that often your friend will have another confidential friend – it does not take long for information to travel if everyone tells just one person.

How you can maintain confidentiality

The most common way in which workers breach confidentiality is by chatting about work with friends or family. It is very tempting to discuss the day's events with your family or with friends over a drink or a meal. This is fine, as it is often therapeutic to discuss a stressful day, or get things into perspective. But you must make it a rule never to mention names.

CARELESS TALK COSTS LIVES

If you always say 'There was this man today …' or 'You won't believe what one of our patients did today …', that is all it takes. Get into the habit of using other characteristics to describe people who appear in your conversation regularly, for example, 'You remember the woman with the very loud voice I told you about last week …'.

When you are out with a group of colleagues, the risks are even greater that you will be tempted to discuss individuals by name. Clearly, your colleagues are already all aware of the individuals, but there is always the likelihood of being overheard in a public place like a pub or restaurant. Again, it is easy to deal with. You just have to make sure that you refer to individuals in a way in which they cannot be identified. The easiest way is to use initials.

It will soon become second nature, and you will find yourself glancing around to make sure you cannot be overheard and referring to individuals by their initials in case conferences and planning meetings!

You will soon become used to maintaining confidentiality, even in relaxed situations with your colleagues.

You also need to be sure that you do not discuss one person you care for with another that you also care for. You may not think you would ever act in that way, but it is so easy to do, with the best of intentions.

Imagine the scene. Someone says 'Ethel doesn't look too good today', and your well-meant response is: 'No, she doesn't. She's had a bit of an upset with her son. She'd probably be really glad of some company later, if you've got the time'. This is the type of response which can cause great distress and, above all, distrust. If the lady you have spoken to later says to Ethel, 'Sue said you were a bit down because of the upset with your son', Ethel is not going to know how much you have said. As far as she knows, you could have given her whole life history to the lady who enquired. The most damaging consequence of this breach of confidentiality is the loss of trust. This can have damaging effects on an individual's self-esteem, confidence and general well-being.

The best way to respond to that comment would be 'Don't you think so? Well, perhaps she might be glad of some company later if you've got the time'.

Check it out

Think of a time when you have told someone something in confidence and later discovered that they had told other people. Try to recall how you felt about it. You may have felt angry or betrayed. Perhaps you were embarrassed and did not want to face anyone. Note down a few of the ways you felt.

Policies of the organisation

Every health and caring organisation will have a policy on confidentiality and the disclosure of information. You must be sure that you know what both policies are in your workplace.

The basic rule is that all information an individual gives, or that is given on his or her behalf, to an organisation is confidential and cannot be disclosed to anyone without the consent of the individual.

Passing on information with consent

There are, however, circumstances in which it may be necessary to pass on information.

In many cases, the passing of information is routine and related to the care of the individual. For example, medical information may be passed to a hospital, to a residential home or to a private care agency. It must be made clear to the individual that this information will be passed on in order to ensure that he or she receives the best possible care.

The key is that only information which is required for the purpose is passed on. For example, it is not necessary to tell the hearing aid clinic that Mr S's son is currently serving a prison sentence. However, if he became seriously ill and the hospital wanted to contact his next of kin, that information would need to be passed on.

Each organisation should have a policy which states clearly the circumstances in which information can be disclosed. According to government guidelines (Confidentiality of Personal Information 1988) the policy should identify:

- ▶ the members of senior management designated to deal with decisions about disclosing information
- ▶ what to do when urgent action is required
- ▶ the safeguards in place to make sure that the information will be used only for the purpose for which it is required
- ▶ arrangements for obtaining manual records and computer records
- ▶ arrangements for reviewing the procedure.

Check it out

Ask your manager about the confidentiality policy in your workplace. Find the procedure and make sure you know how to follow it.

People who need to know

It can be difficult when people claim to have a right or an interest in seeing an individual's records. Of course, there are always some people who do need to know, either because they are directly involved in providing care for the individual or because they are involved in some other support role. However, not everyone needs to know everything, so it is important that information is given on a 'need to know' basis. In other words, people are told what is necessary for them to carry out their role.

Relatives will often claim that they have a 'right to know'. The most famous example of this was Victoria Gillick, who went to court in order to try to gain access to her daughter's medical records. She claimed that she had the right to know if her daughter had been given the contraceptive pill. Her GP had refused to tell her and she took the case all the way to the House of Lords, but the ruling was not changed and she was not given access to her daughter's records. The rules remain the same. Even for close relatives, the information is not available unless the individual agrees.

It is difficult, however, if you are faced with angry or distressed relatives who believe that you have information they are entitled to. One situation you could encounter is where a daughter, for example, believes that she has the right to be told about medical information in respect of her parent. Another example is where someone is trying to find out a person's whereabouts. The best response is to be clear and assertive, but to demonstrate that you understand it is difficult for them. Do not try to 'pass the buck' and give people the idea that they can find out from someone else. There is nothing more frustrating than being passed from one person to another without anyone being prepared to tell you anything. It is important to be clear and say, for example: 'I'm sorry. I know you must be worried, but I can't discuss any information unless your mother agrees', or 'I'm sorry, I can't give out any information about where J is living now. But if you would like to leave me a name and contact details, I will pass on the message and she can contact you'.

Proof of identity

You should always check that people are who they claim to be. It is not unknown for newspaper reporters, unwanted visitors or even a nosey neighbour to claim that they are relatives or professionals from another agency. If basic precautions are not taken to confirm their identity, then they may be able to find out a great deal of confidential information.

Checklist

In person: if you do not know the person who is claiming to have a right to be given information, you should:

▶ find out whether he or she is known to any of your colleagues
▶ ask for proof of identity – if he or she claims to be from another agency involved in providing care, he or she will have an official ID (identity card); otherwise ask to see a driving licence, bank cards, etc.

On the telephone: unless you recognise the voice of the person, you should:

▶ offer to take his or her telephone number and call back after you have checked
▶ if various members of the family or friends are likely to be telephoning about a particular service user, you could arrange a 'password'.

REMEMBER

▶ Generally you should only give information with consent.
▶ Only give people the information they need to know to do their job.
▶ Information should be relevant to the purpose for which it is required.
▶ Check the identity of the person to whom you give information.
▶ Make sure that you do not give information carelessly.

CASE STUDY

Mr R is 59 years old. He is a resident in a nursing home, and he is now very ill. He has Huntington's disease, which is a disease causing dementia, loss of mobility, and loss of speech. It is incurable and untreatable, and it is hereditary. Mr R was divorced many years ago when his children were very young and he has had no contact with his family for over 30 years.

A man who says he is Mr R's son comes to the nursing home in great distress. He is aware, through his mother, that his paternal grandfather died 'insane' and he has now heard about his father being in a nursing home. He is terrified that his father has a hereditary disease and that he also may have it. He has young children and is desperate to know if they are at risk.

1 What can you tell Mr R's son?
2 Does he have a right to know?
3 What do you think should happen?
4 Whose rights are your concern?

Computer records must be surrounded by proper security.

Looking after information

Once something is written down or entered on a computer, it becomes a permanent record. For this reason, you must be very careful what you do with any files, charts, notes or other written records. They must always be stored somewhere locked and safe. People should be very careful with files which leave the workplace. There are many stories about files being stolen from cars or left on buses!

Records kept on computers must also be kept safe and protected. Your workplace will have policies relating to records on computers, which will include access being restricted by a password, and the computer system being protected against the possibility of people 'hacking' into it.

Since the Access to Personal Files Act 1987, individuals can see their personal files. This means that people can see their medical records, or social services files from the date of the Act. Obviously, people are only entitled to see information about themselves, and they cannot see any part of their record which relates to someone else.

The information which you write in files should be clear and useful. Do not include irrelevant information, and write only about the individual concerned. Anything you write should be true and able to be justified, as the two examples below show.

> Name: A. Person
>
> Mr P settling back well after discharge from hosp. Fairly quiet and withdrawn today. Son to visit in AM. Report from hosp included in file, prognosis not good. Not able to get him to talk today, for further time tomorrow.

> Name: J. Soap
>
> Joe visited new flat today. Very positive and looking forward to move. No access problems, delighted with purpose-built kitchen and bathroom. Further visit from OT needed to check on any aids required. Confirmed with housing assoc. that Joe wants tenancy. Will send tenancy agreement, should start on 1st.
>
> Need to check: housing benefit, OT visit, notify change of address to Benefits Agency, PACT team, etc., shopping trip with Joe for any household items.

Key to good practice

The purpose of a file is to reflect an accurate and up-to-date picture of an individual's situation, and to provide an historical record which can be referred to at some point in the future. Some of it may be required to be disclosed to other agencies. Always think about what you write. Make sure it is ACES:

Accurate
Clear
Easy to read
Shareable.

All information, however it is stored, is subject to the rules laid down in the Data Protection Act 1998, which covers medical records, social service records, credit information, local authority information – in fact, anything which is personal data (facts and opinions about an individual).

The principles of data protection

Anyone processing personal data must comply with the eight enforceable principles of good practice. These say that data must be:

- fairly and lawfully processed
- processed for limited purposes
- adequate, relevant and not excessive
- accurate
- not kept longer than necessary
- processed in accordance with the data subject's rights
- kept secure
- not transferred to countries without adequate protection.

Written records

The confidentiality of written records is extremely important. You will need to make sure that, when you receive information in a written form (perhaps intended for somebody's file or a letter concerning somebody you are caring for), the information is not left where it could be easily read by others.

Do not leave confidential material lying around in public areas.

Do not leave confidential letters or notes lying in a reception area, or on a desk where visitors or other staff members might see them. You should ensure that the information is filed, or handed to the person it is intended for, or that you follow your agency procedure for handling confidential information as it comes in to the organisation.

You may need to stamp such information with a 'Confidential' stamp so that people handle it correctly.

Telephone

It may be that you will have a telephone request for information, or that you are involved in taking messages over the telephone which concern confidential matters.

▶ You must be very sure that you do not hand out confidential information over the telephone without first checking the identity of the caller.

▶ If necessary, ask for a telephone number and agree to ring the caller back. Just because somebody says that he or she is a social worker, or from a doctor's surgery, or from another care organisation, does not necessarily mean that is the case.

▶ You have a duty to check a person's identity and his or her rights to any information before you hand it out.

▶ A great deal of information about individuals which ought to be confidential is inadvertently handed out over the telephone to unauthorised people simply because they have claimed to work in a particular setting or claimed to have a right to the information.

▶ If you are unsure as to how much you should tell someone, take the telephone number and offer to call back, then check with your supervisor.

Key to good practice

The basic rule when you are asked for information is:

Do not give any information without seeking the consent of the individual concerned, unless you know that the caller has a right to have that information and a need to know it.

Faxes

Fax machines present a different type of problem in terms of confidentiality of information coming into any work setting. Many agencies and organisations have a fax machine at a central point. This can often mean that incoming faxes are received in a very public area and can be left lying in the fax tray or can be read by anybody who happens to be standing in the office.

Check it out

Your organisation should have a policy for dealing with incoming faxes. It is important that you check what this policy is and discuss it with your supervisor. Ensure that you follow whatever guidelines are in place for maintaining confidentiality of faxed information.

Organisational information

Obviously, there is some information which callers may ask for which is generally available to the public, such as visiting times, directions to your place of work, and so on.

In most places of work this sort of information is readily available and given to anyone who asks. However, if you work in a women's refuge, for example, certainly the address or telephone number will not be given out to anyone who asks for it. So there are always considerations to take into account before passing on information, and you should always check if you are unsure.

Keys to good practice

✔ Always check before giving out any information concerning an individual.
✔ Never leave confidential information in a place where it can be seen.
✔ Make sure that confidential information is marked as such.

The dos and don'ts of dealing with information

Type of information	Do	Don't
Telephone calls, incoming	Check the identity of the caller	Give out any information unless you are sure who the caller is
Telephone calls, outgoing	Make sure that you are passing on information to which the caller is entitled	Give out details that the individual has not agreed to disclose
Written information	Check that it goes immediately to the person it is intended for	Leave written information lying around where it can be read by anyone
Receiving faxed material	Check your organisation's procedure for dealing with faxed material. Collect it as soon as possible from any central fax point	Leave it in a fax tray where it could be read by unauthorised people
Sending faxed material	Ensure that is clearly marked 'Confidential' and has the name on it of the person to whom it should be given	Fax confidential material without clearly stating that it is confidential and it is only to be given to a named person If in doubt, do not use a fax to send confidential information
Receiving e-mailed information	Save any confidential attachments or messages promptly into a password-protected file Acknowledge safe receipt of confidential information	Leave an e-mail open on your screen

Type of information	Do	Don't
Sending e-mailed information	Ensure that you have the right e-mail address for the person who is receiving the information Clearly mark the e-mail 'Confidential' if it contains personal information Ask for the recipient to acknowledge receipt	Leave an e-mail open on your screen Send confidential information to an address without a named mailbox, e.g. info@ ...

How to refuse to give information

It can be quite hard to refuse to give information to someone, especially if he or she is insistent. It is also hard if the person is known to you, perhaps as a relative or friend of a service user. If you are placed in this position, try to remember some simple facts:

▶ The law is on your side.
▶ You must act in your service user's interests, no matter how much you sympathise with the person asking for information.
▶ Be polite, but firm – never allow yourself to be bullied.
▶ If someone becomes rude or aggressive, do not argue – offer to arrange for him or her to speak to a more senior member of staff.
▶ Try saying something like 'I'm sorry, I'm afraid I can't give you that information. Only [name of service user] can give permission for that information to be passed on.'

Choosing the best way to pass on information

Sometimes the method of communication is dictated by the circumstances. If the situation requires an immediate response, or you need to find essential information urgently, then you are unlikely to write a long letter, walk down to the post office, put it in the post and wait until next week to get a reply! You are far more likely to pick up the telephone and see if you can contact the person you need to speak to, or send a quick e-mail. Or you may choose to fax your request, or fax information in response to a telephone request from someone else. These methods are fast, almost instant, and relatively reliable for getting information accurately from one place to another.

There may be other occasions when, on the grounds of confidentiality, something is sent through the post marked 'Strictly confidential' and only to be opened by the person whose name is on the envelope. This method may be entirely appropriate for information which is too confidential to be sent by fax and would be inappropriate in a telephone conversation or to be sent by e-mail.

You will have to take a number of factors into account when deciding which method to use, as the diagram on the next page shows.

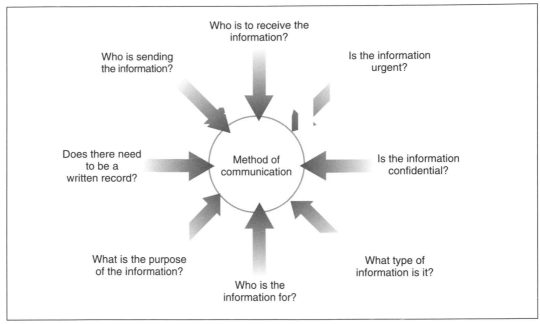

Factors to consider when choosing a method of communication.

When you need to break confidentiality

Passing on information without consent

There are several reasons why decisions about disclosing information without consent may need to be made, and the individual should be informed about what has been disclosed at the earliest possible opportunity. The one exception to this is where information is given in order to assist an investigation into suspected child abuse. In that case, the individual should not be told of any information which has been disclosed until this has been agreed by those carrying out the investigation.

Information may be required by a tribunal, a court or by the ombudsman. Ideally this should be done with the service user's consent, but it will have to be provided regardless of whether the consent is given.

You may have to consider the protection of the community, if there is a matter of public health at stake. You may be aware that someone has an infectious illness, or is a carrier of such an illness and is putting people at risk. For example, if someone was infected with salmonella, but still insisted on going to work in a restaurant kitchen, you would have a duty to inform the appropriate authorities. There are other situations where you may need to give information to the police. If a serious crime is being investigated, the police can ask for information to be given. There is no definition of 'serious', but it is generally accepted as involving:

▶ serious harm to the security of the state or to public order
▶ serious interference with a legal case or investigation
▶ death

- serious injury
- substantial financial gain or financial loss.

Not only can information be requested only in respect of a serious offence, it has to be asked for by a senior-ranking officer, of at least the rank of superintendent.

This means that if the local constable asks if you know whether Mr J has a history of mental health problems, this is not information you are free to discuss.

There may also be times when it is helpful to give information to the media. For example, an elderly confused man, who wanders regularly, may have gone missing for far longer than usual. A description given out on the local radio and in the local paper may help to locate him before he comes to any serious harm.

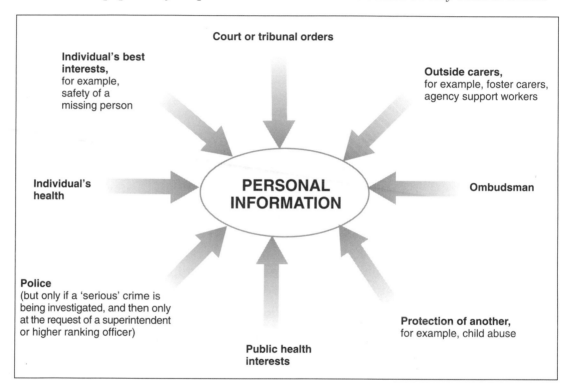

Some reasons why information may be disclosed without consent.

REMEMBER

Disclosure without consent is always a difficult choice. Your decision must be taken in consultation with your supervisor and in line with your organisation's policy. Remember the following main reasons why you may need to do this:

- if it is in the service user's interest
- if there is a serious risk to the community
- if there has been a serious crime, or if the risk of one exists
- in the case of an official/legal investigation.

There are other occasions when it is necessary to pass on information which has been given to you in confidence, or which an individual might expect you to keep confidential. One of the most difficult situations is where a child discloses to you that he or she is being abused. The best practice is to try not to get yourself in the position of agreeing to keep a secret.

Keys to good practice

✔ If you have been given information by a child concerning abuse, you have to pass on the information to your line manager, or whoever is named in the alerting procedures. This is not a matter of choice; even if the child refuses to agree, you have a duty to override his or her wishes. There are no circumstances in which disclosures of abuse of children must be kept confidential.

✔ The situation with an adult, perhaps an older person, who is being abused is different. You can only try to persuade him or her to allow you to pass on the information.

✔ You may be faced with information which indicates that someone intends to harm himself or herself. In that situation, you would be justified in breaking a confidence to prevent harm.

✔ If an individual is threatening to harm someone else, you should pass on the information immediately to your line manager, who will inform the police. It is not appropriate to contact the threatened person directly.

REMEMBER

Decisions about breaking confidentiality are never easy. The following areas are the ones in which you are likely to have to break confidentiality. This is not an exhaustive list, but it covers most of the situations you are likely to encounter:

▶ abuse or exploitation
▶ harm to self
▶ harm to others.

CASE STUDY

Mrs E was in labour, and it was decided that she needed an emergency caesarean section to deliver her baby safely. Her husband was present and everything was explained to him. He was worried, but understood the reason for the surgery. Mrs E signed the consent form for surgery and was hurriedly wheeled down to theatre. Mr E walked beside her to theatre and noticed that there was a stamp on the front of the case notes saying 'High Risk'. He tried to ask one of the staff what this meant just as they were going into the theatre. She said, 'Hang on a second love, I'll be with you in minute. I've just got to put on an extra pair of gloves because of your wife being HIV positive.' Mr E had no idea that his wife was HIV positive.

1 Who was at fault?
2 Should Mr E have been told of his wife's HIV status before this stage?
3 How could this have been prevented?
4 How do you think both of them will be feeling?
5 What lessons can you learn from this?

Listening effectively

Communication is a two-way process. This may sound obvious, but a great deal of communication is wasted because only one of the parties is communicating.

Are you receiving me?

Loud and clear!

Right then, I just need to tell you about …

Think about setting up communication between two radios – when a link is established, the question is asked 'Are you receiving me?' and the answer comes back 'Receiving you loud and clear'. Unfortunately, human beings don't do this exercise before they talk to each other!

If no one is listening and receiving the information a person is trying to communicate, it is just a waste of time. Learning how to listen is a key task for anyone working in care.

You may think that you know how to listen and that it is something you do constantly. After all, you are hearing all sorts of noises all day long – but simply hearing sounds is not the same thing as actively listening.

Check it out

Think about a time you have talked to someone you felt was really interested in what you were saying and listening carefully to you. Try to note down what it was that made you so sure he or she was really listening. Did the fact you thought the person was really listening to you make it easier to talk?

For most people, feeling that someone is really listening makes a huge difference to how confident they feel about talking. You will need to learn about ways in which you can show people you are listening to what they are saying.

Using body language

Although you may think that you do most of your communicating by speaking, you may be surprised to learn that over 80% of what you communicate to others is understood without you speaking a word. Body language, or non-verbal communication, is the way in which we pick up most of the messages people are trying to give us – and some that they're not!

The way in which you use your body can convey messages about:

▶ your feelings
▶ your attitudes
▶ your intentions
▶ your interest
▶ your concern
▶ your attention.

The messages are made clear by such things as facial expression, or maintaining eye contact; sitting forward when you are listening; or having an open and relaxed posture.

REMEMBER

Body language backs up the words you use – or body language can make a liar of you!

Yes, I'm really interested, go on

You can tell me anything, I'm very friendly and approachable

No, it's fine, I've got plenty of time – don't feel you have to hurry

Your body language will let people know that you are really listening to what they are saying. Practise your listening skills in just the same way you would practise any other skill – you can learn to listen well.

Always:

▶ look at the person who is talking to you
▶ maintain eye contact, but without staring
▶ nod your head to encourage the person to talk and show that you understand
▶ use 'aha', 'mm' and similar expressions which indicate that you are still listening

- lean slightly towards the person who is speaking – this indicates interest and concern
- have an open and interested facial expression, which should reflect the tone of the conversation – happy, serious, etc.

Using verbal communication

Body language is one key to effective listening, but what you say in reply is also important. You can back up the message that you are interested and listening by checking that you have understood what has been said to you. Using phrases beginning 'so …' to check that you have got it right can be helpful. 'So … it's only since you had the fall that you are feeling worried about being here alone.' 'So … you were happy with the service before the hours were changed.'

You can also use expressions such as 'So what you mean is …' or 'So what you are saying is …'

Short, encouraging phrases used while people are talking can show concern, understanding or sympathy. Phrases such as 'I see', 'Oh dear', 'Yes', or 'Go on' all give the speaker a clear indication that you are listening and want him or her to continue.

Using questions

Sometimes questions can be helpful to prompt someone who is talking, or to try to move a conversation forward. There are two different kinds of questions. Questions that can be answered with just 'yes' or 'no' are **closed questions**. 'Would you like to go out today?' is a closed question.

An **open question** needs more than 'yes' or 'no' to answer it. 'What is your favourite kind of outing?' is an open question. Open questions usually being with:

- what
- how
- why
- when
- where.

Depending on the conversation and the circumstances, either type of question may be appropriate. For example, if you are encouraging someone to talk because he or she has always been quiet, but has suddenly begun to open up, you are more likely to use open questions to encourage him or her to carry on talking. On the other hand, if you need factual information or you just want to confirm that you have understood what has been said to you, then you may need to ask closed questions.

Check it out

What type of question is each of the following:

- ▶ 'Are you feeling worried?'
- ▶ 'What sort of things worry you?'
- ▶ 'Do you want to join in the games tonight?'
- ▶ 'Is your daughter coming to visit?'
- ▶ 'Why were you cross with Marge this morning?'
- ▶ 'Were you cross with Marge this morning?'
- ▶ 'What have you got planned for when your daughter comes to visit?'
- ▶ 'Do you live here alone?'
- ▶ 'How do you feel about living alone?'

One of the main points to remember when listening is that whatever you say, there should not be too much of it! You are supposed to be listening, not speaking. Some DON'T's for good listening:

- ▶ Don't interrupt – always let people finish what they are saying, and wait for a gap in the conversation
- ▶ Don't give advice – even if asked. You are not the person concerned, so you cannot respond to questions which start 'If you were me …'. Your job is to encourage people to take responsibility for their own decisions, not to tell them what to do!
- ▶ Don't tell people about your own experiences. Your own experiences are relevant to you because they teach you about the kind of person you are, but your role is to listen to others, not talk about yourself.
- ▶ Don't ever dismiss fears, worries or concerns by saying 'that's silly …' or 'you shouldn't worry about that'. People's fears are real and should not be made to sound trivial.

Check it out

Think about two particular occasions when you have been involved in communicating with service users. Write a brief description of the circumstances, and then write notes on how you showed the service users that you were listening to them. If you have not yet had enough experience of working with service users to be able to think of two occasions, think about times when you have listened effectively to a friend or relative and write about that instead.

Outcome activity 2.1

Communicating with others is an essential part of effective work in care, but communication may not always be straightforward. Work in pairs for this activity.

Step 1
Look again at the case study on page 108 and the questions which follow.

Step 2
Sit down with your partner and go through the answers you have decided upon, explaining why you have given them. You should plan to talk for at least 5 minutes. Your partner's job is to listen to you and to respond appropriately to what you are saying. Swap roles and listen to your partner doing the same thing.

Step 3
Make notes about how well your partner communicated. Was he or she clear? Did he or she:

▶ speak at a level and speed you could understand?
▶ make eye contact?
▶ get a message across?

Step 4
Make notes about how you felt when your partner was listening to you. Did you feel that he or she was interested? Were you encouraged to talk? Or did you feel rushed, or that he or she was not very interested?

Step 5
Give feedback to your partner on how well he or she communicated and listened to you. Have your partner give feedback to you.

In your role as a care professional, you will often be in a position where you need to be part of a formal group for a range of different purposes. This could be:

▶ a case conference or review
▶ a planning meeting
▶ a shift handover
▶ a staff meeting
▶ a service user group.

Formal groups are different from those which are less structured and are usually formed for specific reasons, in order to achieve a particular objective or aim. Informal groups can be groups of colleagues or friends, family groups or people with similar interests or hobbies.

Roles in groups

Depending on the way the group works and its purpose, there may be different roles for the group members. If the group is ongoing, such as a management committee, a fundraising committee or a campaign committee, or a permanent body dealing with different issues such as a child protection conference or a regular review committee, people are likely to hold particular positions. These will vary depending on the nature of the group, but are likely to include the ones shown in the table on the next page.

Position	Role
Chair	Runs the meetings, keeps order, makes sure people have a chance to speak, sums up debates and discussions and ensures that decisions are reached
Secretary	Deals with correspondence, ensures that all members of the group have necessary information, sends out notices of group meetings, records the discussions and keeps a record (minutes)
Professional representative	Role will vary depending on the group, but provides specific professional advice and information
Treasurer	If the group is a fundraising or campaigning group or a management committee, a treasurer will maintain the financial records of the group

Making group communication effective

Without good communication it is not possible to have an effective group. Each group member may have a different style of communication and it is important that all of the group members are able to relate to each other, even if the style of communication is different. Some people communicate openly and are happy to share their feelings and concerns, but others may find it harder to discuss feelings and will need encouragement and support within the group to enable them to do so. The different styles of communication that you may see among group members could be:

▶ open, sharing and clear
▶ secretive, unwilling to share information
▶ aggressive, dominating, wanting to override the views of others and to impose their own views on the workings of the group
▶ lacking confidence, finding it difficult to express any views, unassertive and unable to share ideas and suggestions with the group
▶ manipulative, trying to control the group in a less obvious way than the aggressive person
▶ negative, only seeing the problems in every situation and never able to offer a constructive idea or suggestion.

You will need to recognise the value of each different style of communication within your group and to appreciate that every group member, regardless of the way in which he or she communicates, will have something valuable to bring to group meetings. It will be important for the effectiveness of the group that group meetings and communications take account of the range of ways in which people function within the group. It is important to make sure that information is shared in such a way that each member is able to use it well, and that all members are able to make a contribution in the way in which they feel comfortable.

For example, if the group is a work team discussing ideas for a new project or how a particular event will be organised and take place, then contributions should be sought from team members in a way which allows everyone to contribute. If there are people in the group who tend to be unassertive and quiet in meetings, then the request for ideas and contributions could be posted on the staff notice board some days before, and contributions could be submitted in writing. This will give an unassertive group member the chance to make some notes which can be circulated to other team members. If one member tends to dominate and take over in group discussions, this will have to be challenged if it is damaging the functioning of the group.

Making a presentation

In some group settings you may be asked to make a presentation about important aspects of a new development or progress on a project. There are several ways to make presentations, from simple and basic to the use of sophisticated high-tech equipment.

Whatever the style of your presentation you need to use the same communication skills.

▸ Make sure you have included all the information you need to get across.
▸ Do not include unnecessary detail.
▸ Give people clear notes or handouts of all the essential information points.
▸ Speak clearly and not too quickly.
▸ Look around your audience, making passing eye contact.
▸ Decide whether you want questions during your presentation – if not, ask people to keep questions until the end.

There are different styles of presentation, but you will always need the same communication skills.

- Give a broad overview to introduce your subject, then break down the headings to give details. Finish by summing up and drawing any conclusions.
- Be observant – notice if your audience looks interested or if people are bored and fidgeting. If so, you need to get moving and wind up!
- Make your remarks short and clear rather than long and rambling.

Documentation

Most meetings involving groups will result in paperwork. Some of the written work is produced before the meeting and some after it.

Paperwork	Details
Notice of meeting	Information about the date, time and venue for the meeting
Agenda	List of matters to be discussed at the meeting
Minutes	Record of what was said and decided at the meeting
Action list	Details of actions to be taken following a meeting, with the name or initials of the person responsible for carrying them out
Report	If the meeting is about a service user, it is usual to produce a report which can be circulated to all those concerned

Recording decisions from a review or planning meeting

The outcome of any meeting to discuss care or how to meet a service user's needs must be carefully recorded. Service users' needs could be:

- educational – for example, selection of appropriate school or college provision, access to information about services or systems
- recreational – identifying activities and opportunities to pursue interests
- financial – identifying needs for budgeting or obtaining additional income
- physical – a wide range depending on the service user's circumstances
- legal or advocacy – identifying or enabling access to advice and support services or to solicitors or barristers via the Legal Aid system if necessary
- social – accessing companions and friends
- emotional – for love and close relationships.

It is likely that your work setting will have a specific format for recording decisions, but if not, careful minutes must be taken of the meeting and all of the conclusions reached must be recorded. It is important that the discussions at the meeting are briefly recorded, so that people who have taken part in the meeting know their contribution has been noted, but the key is to have a clear record of all final decisions.

The form which your work setting already has, or any documents which you may develop, may look like the one below.

Record of care planning decisions

Service user name	Date of meeting

Those present at meeting

Main points of discussion

Decisions

Please show each decision with a separate number, e.g. 1, 2, 3, a, b, c.

Confidentiality

Where documents relate to any service user they should of course be kept strictly confidential. There will be certain people who have a need to know the information, however. It will be important to make sure that the information recorded from a meeting is circulated to all who were present, and those who were not present at the meeting but have a need to know the outcome. The most important person to receive a copy of this information is the service user, regardless of whether he or she was present at the care planning meeting.

Information about decisions should also go to any carers or relatives whom the service user has indicated should be involved, and to the relevant health or other care professionals who are working with the service user. You must ensure that the service user is aware of the fact that this information will be circulated to those who need to know, and you must take his or her views into account if there are particular people the service user does not wish to receive the information.

Outcome activity 2.2

Your task is to prepare a report for a review meeting or case conference, and to make the presentation. If you do not have access to such a meeting, you can do this task as a role play in a group of colleagues.

Step 1
Consider whether you are working with a service user about whom you could prepare a study or report. If so, make sure that you have the service user's agreement and also your supervisor's or manager's. Use only initials when referring to the person in your report, and do not include any information which could identify him or her.

If you are not able to prepare a report on a real service user, use a character from a TV soap or a film or book, or make one up.

Step 2
Prepare your report, including a full history with as much about the family background as you can find. Include information about the service user's present circumstances, and what is likely to happen to him or her in the future. If you are describing a fictional character, you will have to use your imagination to make up the details.

Try to use a computer programme such as PowerPoint to prepare your presentation, and note all the relevant points on slides. You can then give your audience handouts to support the slides.

If you are in an real meeting, you will have to prepare the report in the way that is usual for that meeting. This is likely to be a short written report with a verbal presentation at the meeting.

Step 3
Present your report to a staff group or conference, or perform your role play within a group of colleagues.

Step 4
Ask the group for feedback on your presentation/report. You can ask for verbal feedback, or invite written feedback by preparing a questionnaire. Make sure that you ask for feedback on the following areas:

- clarity
- suitability of presentation materials
- usefulness of handouts/notes
- level and speed of presentation.

Promote effective communication with people where there are communication differences

Communication differences

This outcome deals with communication where there are differences between the worker and an individual that can cause problems. Communication differences include:

▶ people speaking different languages
▶ either the worker or the individual having a sensory impairment
▶ distress, where somebody is so upset that he or she is unable to communicate
▶ a physical illness or disability, such as a stroke or confusion
▶ cultural differences.

Language

Where an individual speaks a different language from those who are providing care, it can be an isolating and frustrating experience. The individual may become distressed and frightened as it is very difficult to establish exactly what is happening and he or she is not in a position to ask or to have any questions answered. The person will feel excluded from anything happening in the care setting and will find making relationships with carers extremely difficult. There is the possibility that misunderstanding will occur.

Hearing loss

A loss or reduction of ability to hear clearly can cause major differences in the ability to communicate.

Communication is a two-way process, and it is very difficult for somebody who does not hear sounds at all or hears them in a blurred and indistinct way to be able to respond and to join in. The result can be that people become withdrawn and feel very isolated and excluded from others around them. This can lead to frustration and anger. As a result, people may present some quite challenging behaviour.

Profound deafness is not as common as partial hearing loss. People are most likely to suffer from loss of hearing of certain sounds at certain volumes or at certain pitches, such as high sounds or low sounds. It is also very common for people to find it difficult to hear if there is background noise – many sounds may jumble together, making it very hard to pick out the voice of one person. Hearing loss can also have an effect on speech, particularly for those who are profoundly deaf and are unable to hear their own voices as they speak. This can make communication doubly difficult.

Visual impairment

Visual impairment causes many communication difficulties. Not only is an individual unable to pick up the visual signals which are being given out by someone who is speaking, but, because he or she is unaware of these signals, the person may also fail to give appropriate signals in communication. This lack of non-verbal communication and lack of ability to receive and interpret non-verbal communication can lead to misunderstandings about somebody's attitudes and behaviour. It means that a person's communications can easily be misinterpreted, or it could be thought that he or she is behaving in an inappropriate way.

Physical disability

Depending on the disability, this can have various effects. People who have suffered strokes, for example, will often have communication difficulties, not only in forming words and speaking, but they often also suffer from aphasia (or dysphasia), which is the inability to understand and to express meaning through words. They lose the ability to find the right words for something they want to say, or to understand the meanings of words said to them. This condition is very distressing for the individual and for those who are trying to communicate. Often this is coupled with a loss of movement and a difficulty in using facial muscles to form words.

In some cases, the communication difficulty is a symptom of a disability. For example, many people with cerebral palsy and motor neurone disease have difficulty in controlling the muscles that affect voice production, and speaking in a way which can be readily understood becomes very difficult. Other disabilities may have no effect at all upon voice production or the thought processes that produce spoken words, but the lack of other body movements may mean that non-verbal communication may be difficult or not what you would expect.

Learning disabilities

These may, dependent upon their severity, cause differences in communication in terms of the level of understanding of the individual and his or her ability to respond appropriately to any form of communication. This will vary depending on the degree of learning disability of the individual, but broadly the effect of learning disabilities is to limit the ability of an individual to understand and process information given to him or her. It is also possible that individuals will have a short attention span, so this may mean that communications have to be repeated several times in an appropriate form.

Dementia/confusion

This difficult and distressing condition is most prevalent in older people and people who suffer from Alzheimer's disease. The confusion can result ultimately in the loss of the ability to communicate, but in the early stages it involves short-term memory loss to the extent of being unable to remember the essential parts of a conversation or a recent exchange. It can necessitate the constant repetition of any form of communication.

Cultural differences

People's communication differences can result from differences in culture and background. Culture is about more than language – it is about the way that people live, think and relate to each other. In some cultures, for example, children are not allowed to speak in the presence of certain adults. Other cultures do not allow women to speak to men they do not know.

Some people may have been brought up in a background or in a period of time when challenging authority by asking questions was not acceptable. Such people may find it very hard to ask questions of doctors or other health professionals and are unlikely to feel able to raise any queries about how their care or treatment should be carried out.

REMEMBER

Communication differences can result as much from differences in attitude as they can from differences in language.

Check it out

Try renting a video in a language other than your own, or watch a subtitled film on TV, covering the lower part of the TV screen where the subtitles are. Try to make sense of what is shown in the film. Note how difficult it is to understand what is happening and how frustrating it is. Notice how quickly you lose interest and decide that you will not bother to watch any more. Imagine how that feels if you are ill or in need of care, and everyone around you is speaking in a language you do not understand.

Effects of communication differences

The most common effect of communication differences is for the person receiving care to feel frustrated and isolated. It is an important part of your job to do everything in your power to reduce the effect of communication differences and to try to lessen the feelings of isolation and frustration that people experience.

CASE STUDY

Mrs C is 75 years old. She is Chinese and lives with her son and daughter-in-law in England. She has lived in England for over 30 years, but speaks no English and very rarely goes out apart from shopping within the local Chinese community. Mrs C has now developed a potentially life-threatening, but operable, bowel cancer. She is to have a series of tests which will be followed by surgery, a likely colostomy and radiotherapy. Her son is able to translate during the visits to the hospital, but he will not be able to remain with her during the entire time of her hospital stay.

1 How do you think Mrs C will be feeling?
2 If you were looking after her in hospital, what would be your first step to communicating with her?
3 What are the issues for her in having her son translate in these circumstances?
4 How could her condition be affected by poor communication?

How to find out about likely communication problems

You can discover likely communication problems by simply observing an individual. You can find out a great deal about how a person communicates and what the differences are between his or her way of communicating and your own.

Observation should be able to establish:

▶ which language is being used
▶ if the service user experiences any hearing difficulties or visual impairment
▶ if there is any physical illness or disability
▶ if there is a learning disability.

Any of these factors could have a bearing on how well a person will be able to communicate with you, and what steps you may need to take to make things easier. Observation will give you some very good clues to start with, but there are other useful sources of information for establishing exactly what a particular individual needs to assist communication. You may consider:

▶ asking the individual where this is possible – he or she is likely to be your best source of information
▶ discussing with colleagues who have worked with the individual before and who are likely to have some background information and advice
▶ consulting other professionals who have worked with the individual and may have knowledge of means of communication which have been effective for them
▶ reading previous case notes or case histories
▶ finding out as much as you can about an individual's particular illness or disability, where you have been able to establish this – the most useful

sources of information are likely to be the specialist agencies for the particular condition

▶ talking to family or friends. They are likely to have a great deal of information about what the differences in communication are for the individual. They will have developed ways of dealing with communication, possibly over a long period of time, and are likely to be a very useful source of advice and help.

How to record information

There would be little point in finding out about effective means of communication with someone and then not making an accurate record so that other people can also communicate with that person.

You should find out your employer's policy on where such information is to be recorded – it is likely to be in the service user's case notes.

Be sure that you record:

▶ the nature of the communication differences
▶ how they show themselves
▶ ways which you have found to be effective in overcoming the differences.

Information recorded in notes may look like this:

Mr P has communication difficulties following his stroke. He is aphasic, with left side haemaplaegia. Speech is slurred but possible to understand with care. Most effective approaches are:

a) allow maximum time for communication responses

b) modify delivery if necessary in order to allow understanding

c) speak slowly, with short sentences

d) give only one piece of information at a time

e) physical reassurance (holding and stroking hand) seems to help while waiting for a response

f) can use flashcards on bad days (ensure they are placed on the right-hand side)

g) check Mr P has understood the conversation.

Keys to good practice

✔ Check what the differences in communication are.
✔ Remember they can be cultural as well as physical.
✔ Examine the effects of the communication differences for a particular individual.
✔ Use all possible sources to obtain information.

Overcoming language differences in communication

Where you are in the position of providing care for someone who speaks a different language from you, it is clear that you will need the services of an interpreter for any serious discussions or communication.

▶ Your work setting is likely to have a contact list of interpreters.
▶ Social services departments and the police have lists of interpreters.
▶ The embassy or consulate for the appropriate country will also have a list of qualified interpreters.

You should always use professional interpreters wherever possible. It may be very tempting to use other members of the family – very often children have excellent language skills – but it is inappropriate in most care settings. This is because:

▶ their English and their ability to interpret may not be at the same standard as a professional interpreter, and misunderstandings can easily occur
▶ you may wish to discuss matters which are not appropriate to be discussed with children, or the individual may not want members of his or her family involved in very personal discussions about health or care issues.

It is unlikely that you would be able to have a full-time interpreter available throughout somebody's period of care, so it is necessary to consider alternatives for encouraging everyday communication.

Be prepared to learn words in the individual's language which will help communication. You could try to give the person some words in your language if he or she is willing and able to learn them.

There are other simple techniques that you may wish to try which can help basic levels of communication. For example, you could use flashcards and signals, similar to those which you would use for a person who has suffered a stroke. This gives the person the opportunity to show a flashcard to indicate his or her needs. You can also use them to find out what kind of assistance may be needed.

The suggestions shown on the next page are not exhaustive and you will come up with many which are appropriate for the individual and for your particular care setting. They are a helpful way of assisting with simple communication and allowing people to express their immediate physical needs.

Some of the flashcards you may use.

The most effective way of communicating with a person who speaks a different language is through non-verbal communication. A smile and a friendly face are understood in all languages, as are a concerned facial expression and a warm and welcoming body position.

However, be careful about the use of gestures – gestures which are acceptable in one culture may not be acceptable in all. For example, an extended thumb in some cultures would mean 'great, that's fine, OK', but in many cultures it is an extremely offensive gesture. If you are unsure which gestures are acceptable in another culture, make sure that you check before using any which may be misinterpreted.

Overcoming hearing difficulties in communication

▶ Ensure that any means of improving hearing which an individual uses, for example a hearing aid, is working properly and is fitted correctly, that the batteries are working, that it is clean and that it is doing its job properly in terms of improving the individual's hearing.

▶ Ensure that you are sitting in a good light, not too far away and that you speak clearly, but do not shout. Shouting simply distorts your face and makes it more difficult for a person with hearing loss to be able to read what you are saying.

Some people will lip read, while others will use a form of sign language for understanding. This may be BSL (British Sign Language) or MAKATON, which uses signs and symbols. They may rely on a combination of lip reading and gestures.

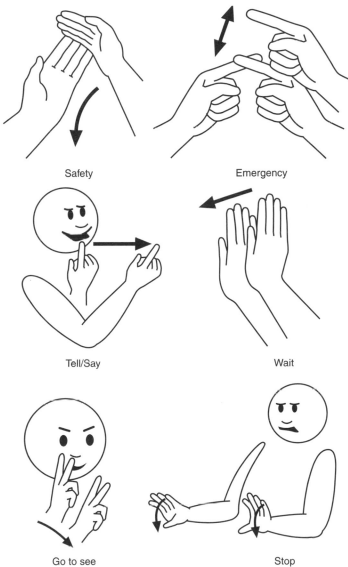

BSL signs.

REMEMBER

If you are able to learn even simple signing or the basic rules of straightforward spoken communication with people who have hearing loss, you will significantly improve the way in which they are able to relate to their care environment.

Other services which are extremely helpful to people who have hearing difficulties are telecommunication services, such as using a minicom or typetalk service. These allow a spoken conversation to be translated into written form using a form of typewriter, and the responses can be passed in the same way by an operator who will relay them to the hearing person. These services have provided a major advance in enabling people who are hard of hearing or profoundly deaf to use telephone equipment. For people who are less severely affected by hearing impairment there are facilities such as raising the volume on telephone receivers to allow them to hear conversations more clearly.

Overcoming visual difficulties in communication

One of the commonest ways of assisting people who have impaired vision is to provide them with glasses or contact lenses. You need to be sure that these are

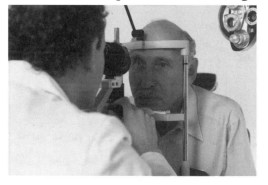

clean and that they are the correct prescription. You must make sure that people have their eyes tested every two years and that their prescription is regularly updated. A person whose eyesight and requirements for glasses have changed will obviously have difficulty in picking up many of the non-verbal signals which you will be giving out when you are communicating with him or her.

For people with more serious loss or impairment, you will need to take other steps to ensure that you minimise the differences that will exist in your styles of communication.

People should have their eyes tested every two years and their prescription should be regularly updated.

Keys to good practice

When communicating with people who have impaired vision:

✔ Do not suddenly begin to speak to someone without first of all letting him or her know that you are there by touching and saying hello.

✔ Make sure that you introduce yourself when you come into a room. It is easy to forget that someone cannot see. A simple 'hello John, it's Sue' is all that is needed so that you don't 'arrive' unexpectedly.

✔ You may need to use touch more than you would in speaking to a sighted person, because the concerns that you will be expressing through your face and your general body movements will not be seen. So, if you are expressing concern or sympathy, it may be appropriate to touch someone's hand or arm, at the same time that you are saying you are concerned and sympathetic.

✔ Ask the individual what system of communication he or she requires – do not impose your idea of appropriate systems on the person. Most people who are visually impaired know very well what they can and cannot do, and if you ask they will tell you exactly what they need you to do.

✔ Do not decide that you know the best way to help. Never take the arm of somebody who is visually impaired to help him or her to move around. Allow the person to take your arm or shoulder, to be guided and tell you where he or she wishes to go.

Overcoming physical disabilities in communication

Physical disability or illness has to be dealt with according to the nature of the disability or the illness. For example, if you were communicating with somebody who had a stroke you would have to work out ways of coping with his or her dysphasia. This is best dealt with by:

▶ using very simple, short sentences, speaking slowly and being prepared to wait while the individual processes what you have said and composes a reply
▶ using gestures – they are helpful in terms of making it easier for people to understand the idea that you are trying to get across
▶ using drawing, writing or flashcards to help understanding
▶ using very simple, closed questions which only need a 'yes' or 'no' answer. Avoid long, complicated sentences with interrelated ideas. For example, do not say: 'It's getting near tea time now, isn't it? How about some tea? Have you thought about what you would like?' Instead, say: 'Are you hungry? Would you like fish? Would you like chicken?' and so on, until you have established what sort of meal the individual would prefer.

Other illnesses, such as motor neurone disease or cerebral palsy, can also lead to difficulties in speech, although not in comprehension.

▶ The individual will understand perfectly what you are saying to him or her but the difficulty will be in communicating with you.
▶ There is no need for you to speak slowly, although you will have to be prepared to allow time for a response owing to the difficulties that the individual will have in producing words.
▶ You will have to become familiar with the sound of the individual's voice and the way in which he or she communicates. It can be hard to understand people who have illnesses which affect their facial, throat or larynx muscles.

Overcoming learning disabilities in communication

Where people have a learning disability, you will need to adjust your methods of communicating to take account of the level of disability that they experience. You should have gathered sufficient information about the individual to know the level of understanding that he or she has – how simply and how often you need to explain things and the kinds of communication which are likely to be the most effective.

Many people with a learning disability respond well to physical contact and are able to relate and

Many people with a learning disability are able to communicate on a physical level more easily than on a verbal level.

communicate on a physical level more easily than on a verbal level. This will vary between individuals and you should be prepared to use a great deal of physical contact and hugs when communicating with people who have a learning disability.

Overcoming cultural differences in communication

Communication is about much more than words being exchanged between two people – it is influenced by a great many factors. The way in which people have been brought up and the society and culture that they live in have a great effect on the way in which they communicate.

For example, some cultures use gestures or touch much more than others. In some cultures it is acceptable to stand very close to someone, whereas in others people feel extremely uncomfortable if someone stands too close. You need to find out about the person's background when you are thinking about how you can make communication work for him or her. To find out the information you need, you could:

▶ look in the person's records
▶ speak to a member of the family or a friend, if this is possible

▶ ask someone else from the same culture, either a colleague or through the country's cultural representatives (contact the embassy or consulate and ask for the information) – alternatively you could try a local multicultural organisation
▶ use reference books, if necessary.

It is also important that you communicate with people at the correct intellectual level. Make sure that you communicate with them at a language level which they are likely to understand, but not find patronising. For example, older people and people who have disabilities have every right to be spoken to as adults and not patronised or talked down to. One of the commonest complaints from people with physical disabilities is that people will talk to their carers about them rather than talk to them directly – this is known as the 'does he take sugar' approach.

> ## Check it out
>
> Find out the policy in your workplace for checking on people's cultural preferences. Ask who establishes the information about the cultural background of people who use your service, and what the policies are to ensure their needs are met.

Unit 2 Effective communication

Making sure you have been understood

Although it is unacceptable to talk down to people, it is pointless trying to communicate with them by using so much jargon and medical terminology that they don't understand anything you have said. You must be sure that your communication is being understood. The most straightforward way to do this is to ask someone to recap on what you have discussed.

You could say something like: 'Can we just go over this so that we are both sure about what is happening – you tell me what is happening tomorrow'. Alternatively you can rephrase what you have just said and check with the individual that he or she has understood. For example:

'The bus is coming earlier than usual tomorrow because of the trip. It will be here at eight o'clock instead of nine – is that OK?'

'Yes.'

'So, you're sure that you can be up and ready by eight o'clock to go on the trip?'

Communication through actions

For many people, it is easier to communicate by actions than by words. You will need to make sure that you respond in an appropriate way by recognising the significance of a touch or a sudden movement from somebody who is ill and bedridden, or a gesture from somebody who speaks a different language. A gesture can indicate what his or her needs are and what sort of response the person is looking for from you. You may be faced with a young person with challenging behaviour who throws something at you – this is a means of communication. It may not be a very pleasant one, but nonetheless, it expresses much of the person's hurt, anger and distress. It is important that you recognise this for what it is and respond in the same way you would if that person had been able to express his or her feelings in words.

REMEMBER

If you are planning communication with somebody who has a sensory impairment or who has a learning disability, you will need to take account of this and adjust your communication so that it is at a level he or she is able to understand and make sense of. The single most important factor in communicating is that you are understood.

Encouraging communication

The best way to ensure that somebody is able to communicate to the best of his or her ability is to make the person feel as comfortable and as relaxed as possible. There are several factors to consider when thinking about how to make people feel confident enough to communicate. They are summarised in the table below.

Communication difference	Encouraging actions
Different language	▶ Smile ▶ Have a friendly facial expression ▶ Use gestures ▶ Use pictures ▶ Show warmth and encouragement – repeat their words with a smile to check understanding
Hearing impairment	▶ Speak clearly, listen carefully, respond to what is said to you ▶ Remove any distractions and other noises ▶ Make sure any aids to hearing are working ▶ Use written communication where appropriate ▶ Use signing where appropriate and understood ▶ Use properly trained interpreter if high level of skill is required
Visual impairment	▶ Use touch to communicate concern, sympathy and interest ▶ Use tone of voice rather than facial expressions to communicate mood and response ▶ Do not rely on non-verbal communication, e.g. facial expression or nodding head ▶ Ensure that all visual communication is transferred into something which can be heard, either a tape or somebody reading
Confusion or dementia	▶ Repeat information as often as necessary ▶ Keep re-orientating the conversation if you need to ▶ Remain patient ▶ Be very clear and keep conversation short and simple ▶ Use simple written communication or pictures where they seem to help
Physical disability	▶ Ensure that surroundings are appropriate and accessible ▶ Allow for difficulties with voice production if necessary ▶ Do not patronise ▶ Remember that some body language may not be appropriate
Learning disability	▶ Judge appropriate level of understanding ▶ Make sure that you respond at the right level ▶ Repeat things as often as necessary ▶ Remain patient and be prepared to keep covering the same ground ▶ Be prepared to wait and listen carefully to responses

Use signing where it is appropriate and understood.

Key to good practice

The single most important thing that you need to remember is that you must tailor your response to the individual, not the condition.

Stereotyping

Stereotyping people by making generalised assumptions about their abilities is not unusual. There are commonly held views, even among care professionals, about the levels of ability which service users have, based on their disability rather than them as individuals.

If you work with a service user you will need to be aware of the potential views of others and be ready to counteract any stereotyping or labelling which may be taking place. Be aware of the fact that assumptions may be made about the abilities of the service user. For example, it is not uncommon to underestimate what people with learning disabilities can achieve. There is also a commonly held belief that people with Alzheimer's disease need round-the-clock protection. This is not always the case and many people who suffer from Alzheimer's are capable of achieving a great deal of independence, provided that the environment in which they live is suitably adapted. You will need to be aware of the assumptions that may be made, and you should refer back to Unit 1 for details of the ways in which stereotyping and labelling can affect individuals.

CASE STUDY

G is 30 years old and has Down's syndrome. His mother has recently died and his father died two years ago. G had always lived at home and attended a local day-care facility. He also enjoyed socialising at a club which was organised by Mencap on two evenings each week. G had often complained that he was restricted by the very protective attitude of his parents. He wanted to have a more independent existence and to be able to participate in a wide range of sporting and social activities. His parents had always felt that he would be placing himself at risk if they were to agree to his plans to join in this sort of activity.

G has an older brother and two older sisters who have always been supportive of his parents during G's upbringing but none are able to accommodate him full time within their own families. Following the death of their mother they were heavily involved in discussions with the social services department and voluntary agencies about the most appropriate solution to the long-term needs of G.

G was most insistent that he wished to live completely independently and to remain in his own home. He felt that he was perfectly capable of living in this way, and he now intended to take up some of the activities such as hang gliding and parachute jumping which his mother had never allowed him to become involved in. He believed that he was capable of meeting all of his own needs and was unwilling to listen to the concerns of his brother and sisters.

His family, on the other hand, felt that G needed to be in residential care, and they had found a residential facility with a vacancy which was only a few miles from their home town. It would enable G to continue his attendance at his regular day centre and his twice-weekly social club. They felt that this was the only way in which they could ensure that G would be properly cared for and that his safety would be ensured. The family fully intended to continue their regular contact with G and were enthusiastic about the idea of the residential facility. The family were supported in their view by the GP and the staff from the day-care facility which was linked to the residential accommodation. However, the staff from the social club were supportive of G's wishes to extend his independence.

The key worker proposed that G accompany her to look at a supported living situation where six people with a degree of learning disability shared a house and were responsible between them for shopping, cooking and meeting their own needs. They had daily access to a support worker and received a visit each day to provide an agreed level of assistance. This living situation would, within reason, allow G to increase his level of independence and to introduce more risk and challenge into his life.

G and the family (although they had reservations) accepted this as a useful way forward and G moved in and settled happily. He was finally dissuaded from hang gliding and parachute jumping but did become involved in sand yachting, at which he was highly competitive and quite successful. He also frequently assisted as a navigator for one of the drivers in the local car rally club.

1 Why do you think the family felt as they did about G?
2 What may have been the basis for the GP's views in this situation?
3 Examine your own feelings about a young man with a learning disability living in the way G wished to. What is your initial response? What is your response after consideration and reflection on the issues?
4 What was the potential if either the solution proposed by the family or that proposed by G himself had been followed?
5 Whose views were of paramount consideration in this situation?
6 Which of the professionals involved is likely to have the best knowledge of G?
7 What other factors may influence the views of the professionals?

Outcome activity 2.3

You have been asked to work as a communications consultant for a new community centre which is currently being designed. The centre is due to be built in a large market town which forms the centre of a big rural community. Both the town itself and the surrounding area have quite significant numbers of recent immigrants whose first language is not English. There are people from a range of racial backgrounds, and different levels of ability in English.

The new centre is keen to ensure that there is full access to all the facilities for all the people of the area, regardless of their communication needs or their disabilities.

The community centre will have meeting rooms, sports facilities, a community café, computer suite, library and community theatre. Your task is to prepare a report advising the designers about how they can make sure that the communication needs of all the potential users of the centre will be taken into account in the new development.

Step 1
Identify the different groups who may use the centre. Make notes about the communication needs of each group of service users. Think about issues such as language, disability and age.

Step 2
Prepare a plan to make sure that all communication needs are met. Prepare notes about each of the different facilities offered by the new centre and suggest how the needs of each of the groups you have identified could be met.

Step 3
Record your plans and ideas on a spreadsheet, showing each of the different facilities and how the needs of each group of users could be met there.

Reflective practice and development of self and others

As a worker in a care setting, you have a responsibility to constantly review and improve your practice, and to contribute to the development of others. It is the right of service users to expect the best possible quality of care from those who provide it, and high quality care will not be provided unless all practitioners regularly reflect on their own practice and look at ways of improving.

The quality of your own practice is an essential part of the quality of the overall care provided by the organisation for which you work. Each organisation and each individual owes a 'duty of care' to service users. This means that it is your responsibility to make sure that the service provided is the best it can possibly be – this is not an option, but a duty which you accept when you choose to become a professional care worker.

Outcome 1: Reflect on and evaluate own personal effectiveness

Reflective practice

The purpose of reflective practice is to improve and develop your practice by thinking about what you are doing. This sounds simple, but there are many academic theories, models and methods which explain how complex the whole process of learning and reflection is. The important aspect for you and the service users you work with, however, is that you learn from what you do and think carefully about the work you undertake. One of the key starting points for becoming a reflective practitioner is to look carefully at the influences on the way you work, as discussed in Unit 1, Outcome 3 (pages 44–52).

The next stage is to look at your day-to-day work and how well you relate to service users and colleagues. After you have dealt with a difficult situation, or at the end of a shift, you should ask yourself:

▶ how well you approached the situation or your work
▶ the effect your approach appeared to have on those you were working with – both service users and colleagues
▶ whether the quality of the work you produced was sufficiently high.

This will need to be an honest reflection or it is of little value, but you also need to allow for the fact that nobody produces first-class work every day – everyone has days when they are less effective than they would like to be. So do not be too hard on yourself when you are reflecting.

The important thing is to think positively about areas of your work that you can improve. Reflection that does not identify areas for improvement is of little value – in fact, it can be highly destructive.

Learning

When you have identified skills you would like to improve, the next step is to set about learning them. One of the best-known theories about the way in which people learn is the Lewin/Kolb cycle of experiential learning.

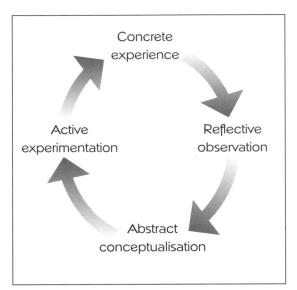

Lewin's cycle.

The learning cycle never stops.

Basically, this cycle means the following.

▶ Something happens to you or you do something; it can an unusual event or something you do every day (**concrete experience**).

▶ You think about it (**reflective observation**).

▶ You work out some general rules about it, or you realise that it fits into a theory or pattern you already know about (**abstract conceptualisation**)

▶ Next time the same situation occurs, you apply your rules or theories (**active experimentation**).

▶ This will make your experience different from the first time, so you will have different factors to think about and different things to learn – so the cycle continues. You never stop learning.

It is easy to see the importance of thinking about what you do – otherwise the cycle of learning will grind to a halt!

Alongside this model, Honey and Mumford (1982) developed a theory about different learning styles. Those who like to experience everything directly (concrete experience) are called **activists**. Those who like to think and reflect (reflective observation) are called **reflectors**. **Theorists** always want to understand all the underlying reasons and concepts (abstract conceptualisation), and **pragmatists** like to have a go and see whether things work (active experimentation).

There are different types of learning for different types of tasks. Some you think about less the better you become (such as typing, knitting or driving). Others need you to think and reflect more, such as all types of professional practice. Models of reflective practice developed by Reynolds (1965) and Dreyfus and Dreyfus (1986) look at the way professional practitioners come to take for granted aspects of practice which they had previously worried about, and move on to reflect on wider issues.

Donald Schon (1983) developed a model of reflective practice which involves recognising the difference between reflecting 'in' action (while you are doing something) and reflecting 'on' action (after the event). This model also involved using a mentor to help and support the process of reflection. The role of mentor is often undertaken by a supervisor or manager, and is invaluable in the process of reflection.

Reflecting is closely connected with learning; you do something, then you reflect on it and learn from it, so that the next time you perform the same task you will do it better and more effectively.

Different ways of learning

Formal training and development are not the only ways you can learn and expand your knowledge and understanding. There are plenty of other ways to keep up progress towards the goals you have set in your personal development plan.

Not everyone learns best from formal training. Other ways people learn are from:

▶ being shown by more experienced colleagues – this is known as 'sitting next to Nellie'
▶ reading textbooks, journals and articles
▶ following up information on the Internet
▶ asking questions and holding professional discussions with colleagues and managers.

Learning by being shown how to do something by more experienced colleagues is known as 'sitting next to Nellie'.

Write down the different ways of learning that you have experienced. Have you, for example, studied a course at college, completed a distance learning programme or attended hands-on training sessions? Tick the learning methods which have been the most enjoyable and most successful for you.

How could you use this information about how you best like to learn in order to update your workplace skills?

Here is a checklist of ways of learning that you might find useful:

- watching other people
- asking questions and listening to the answers
- finding things out for yourself
- going to college and attending training courses
- studying a distance learning course or a course on the Internet.

Methods of reflecting on practice

Undertaking reflection alone is very difficult, so it is important to make use of your supervisor or mentor in order to get feedback on what you have done. Support networks, whether they are formal or informal, are one of the most effective means of identifying areas of your own practice which need further development.

Formal networks

These networks of support are usually put in place by your employer. They are likely to consist of your immediate supervisor and possibly other more senior members of staff on occasion. You are likely to have a regular system of feedback and support meetings, or appraisal sessions with your supervisor. These could be at differing intervals depending on the system in your particular workplace, but are unlikely to be less frequent than once a month.

These systems are extremely useful in giving you the opportunity to benefit from feedback from your supervisor, who will be fully aware of the work you have been doing, and able to identify areas of practice which you may need to improve and areas in which you have demonstrated strength.

The appraisal or supervision system in your workplace may also be the point at which you identify a programme of development which you need to undertake. Some employers identify this at six-monthly or 12-monthly intervals, and some more frequently. Your supervisor is likely to identify which of the available training programmes are appropriate for the areas of your practice which have been identified as needing development.

Getting the most out of supervision

Make sure that you are well prepared for sessions with your supervisor so that you can get maximum benefit from them. This will mean bringing together your reflections on your own practice, using examples and case notes where appropriate. You will need to demonstrate to your supervisor that you have reflected on your own practice and that you have begun identifying areas for development. If you can provide evidence through case notes and records to support this, it will assist your supervisor greatly.

You will also need to be prepared to receive feedback from your supervisor. While feedback is likely to be given in a positive way, this does not mean that it will be uncritical. Many people have considerable difficulty in accepting criticism in any form, even where it is intended to be supportive and constructive. If you are aware that you are likely to have difficulty accepting criticism, try to prepare yourself to view feedback from your supervisor as valuable and useful information which can add to your ability to reflect effectively on the work you are doing.

Check it out

Ask a colleague, or if you don't feel able to do that ask a friend or family member, to offer some constructive criticism on a task you have undertaken – a practical activity such as cooking a meal, or work you have undertaken in the garden or in the house, would be suitable.

If you are able to practise receiving feedback on something which is relatively unthreatening, you are likely to be able to use the same techniques when considering feedback on your working practices.

Your response to negative feedback should not be to defend your actions or to reject the feedback. You must try to accept and value it. A useful reply would be: 'Thank you, that's very helpful. I can use that next time to improve.' If you are able to achieve this you are likely to be able to make the maximum use of opportunities to improve your practice.

On the other hand, if criticism of any kind undermines your confidence and makes it difficult for you to value your own strengths, you should ask your supervisor to identify areas in which you did well, and use the positive to help you respond more constructively to the negative feedback.

Training and development sessions

One of the other formal and organised ways of reflecting on your own practice and identifying strengths, weaknesses and areas for development is during training opportunities. On a course, or at a training day, aspects of your practice and areas of knowledge which are new to you will be discussed, and this will often open up avenues that you had not previously considered. This is one of the major benefits of making the most of all the training and education opportunities that are available to you.

Informal networks

Informal support networks are likely to consist of your work colleagues. These can be major sources of support and assistance. Part of the effectiveness of many teams in many workplaces is their ability to provide useful ideas for improving practice, and support when things go badly.

Informal networks can be major sources of support and assistance.

Some staff teams provide a completely informal and ad-hoc support system, where people give you advice, guidance and support as and when necessary. Other teams will organise this on a more regular basis, and they may get together to discuss specific situations or problems which have arisen for members of the team. You need to be sure that you are making maximum use of all opportunities to gain support, advice and feedback on your practice.

Check it out

Identify any formal and informal support networks in your workplace. Note down the ways in which you use the different types of network and how they support your development. If you identify any gaps or areas where you feel unsupported, discuss this with your supervisor or manager.

Outcome activity 3.1

Step 1

Answer the following questions about yourself. There are no right or wrong answers – they are intended to help you think about the approaches to learning which you find most useful. A discussion with others after you have completed the questions may be interesting, but you should not change any of your answers as a result.

1 Can you get on with tasks:
   ▶ by yourself without anyone to support you?
   ▶ only with someone else there?
   ▶ only if someone is 'nagging' you ?

2 Do you best remember information you have:
   ▶ read?
   ▶ heard?
   ▶ seen?

3 Do you like to learn:
   ▶ alone?
   ▶ in a group?
   ▶ with just a teacher?

4 If you have learned something, do you:
   ▶ remember it?
   ▶ need to keep going back and checking it?
   ▶ need to occasionally go back and check it?

5 Are you curious? Do you prefer:
   ▶ to be given information?
   ▶ to be told where to find information, then find it for yourself?

6 Have you ever:
   ▶ been on a college course?
   ▶ done a distance learning course?
   ▶ been to a training session?

   Which did you find the most enjoyable?
   Which do you remember most from?

Step 2

Research some information about Kolb's learning cycle and the Learning Styles Inventory. You can do the research in a library by using textbooks, or on the Internet.

Step 3

Use the answers to your questions, and the knowledge you have gained from your research, to work out what kind of learner you are and how you learn best.

Step 4

Use the knowledge you have gained about yourself when you are working on your Personal Development Plan (see Outcome Activity 3.2, page 151).

The health and social care sector is one which constantly changes and moves on. New standards reflect the changes in the profession, such as the emphasis on quality services, the focus on tackling exclusion, and the influence of the culture of rights and responsibilities. There has been a huge increase in understanding in all parts of the sector, and a recognition of the satisfaction that comes from working alongside service users as partners and directors of their own care, rather than as passive receivers of services. Developments in technology have brought huge strides towards independence for many service users, thus promoting a changing relationship with carers; at the same time, technological developments have brought different approaches to the way in which work in care is carried out and the administration and recording of service provision.

Legislation and government guidelines are a feature of the work of the sector. Sadly, many of the new guidelines, policies and procedures result from enquiries and investigations which follow tragedies, errors and neglect.

Despite all this, much of what we do in the care sector will remain the same; the basic principles of caring, treating people with dignity and respect, ensuring they have choice and promoting independence will continue, and the skills of good communication remain as vital as ever.

Being aware of new developments

There are many ways in which you can ensure that you keep up to date with new developments in the field of care, and particularly those which affect your own area of work. You should not necessarily assume that your workplace will automatically inform you about new developments, changes and updates which affect your work – you must be prepared to actively maintain your own knowledge base and to ensure that your practice is in line with current thinking and new theories. The best way to do this is to incorporate an awareness of the need to constantly update your knowledge into all your work activities. If you restrict your awareness of new developments to specific times, such as a monthly visit to the library, or a training course every six months, you are likely to miss out on a lot of information.

Sources of information
The media

The area of health and care is always in the news, so it is relatively easy to find out information about new studies and research. You will need to pay attention when watching television programmes or listening to radio news bulletins to find out about new developments, legislation, guidelines and reports related to health and care service users and workers.

Check it out

For one week keep a record of every item which relates to health and care services which you hear on a radio bulletin, see in a television programme, or read in a newspaper. You are likely to be surprised at the very large number of references that you manage to find.

Articles in newspapers and professional journals are excellent sources of information. When reporting on a recently completed study, they usually give information about how to obtain a copy of it.

Conferences

Professional journals also carry advertisements for conferences and training opportunities. You may also find such information in your workplace. There is often a cost involved with attending these events, so the restrictions of the training budget in your workplace may mean that you cannot attend. However, it may be possible for one person to attend and to pass on the information gained to others in the workplace, or to obtain conference papers and hand-outs without attending.

The Internet

The development of information technology, and in particular the Internet, has provided a vast resource for information, views and research.

The Internet can be a useful source of information to help you keep up to date with developments in your field of work.

There are clearly some limitations to using the Internet; for example, many people are reluctant to look for information through that route because they are not confident about using computers. However, if you have access to a computer, using the Internet is a simple process that you could easily learn.

Another disadvantage is that you need to be wary of the information you obtain on the Internet unless it is from an accredited source such as a government department, a reputable university or college, or an established research centre. Make every effort to check the validity of what you are reading. The World Wide Web provides free access to vast amounts of information, but it is an unregulated environment – anyone can publish information on the Internet, and there is no requirement for it to be checked or approved. People can publish their own views and opinions, which may not have any basis in fact. These views and opinions from a wide range of people are valuable and interesting in themselves, but be careful that you do not assume anything to be factually correct unless it is from a reliable source.

Treated with care, the Internet can be one of the speediest and most useful tools in obtaining up-to-date information.

Your supervisor and colleagues

Never overlook the obvious: one of the sources of information which may be most useful to you is also one which is close at hand – your own workplace supervisor and colleagues. They may have many years of experience and accumulated knowledge which they will be happy to share with you. They may also be updating their own practice and ideas, and may have information that they would be willing to share.

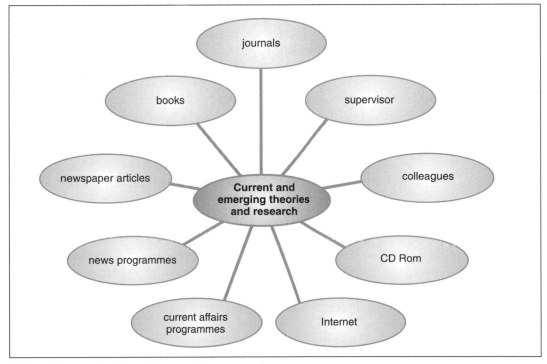

Information can be found from a wide range of sources.

Understanding new information

Reading and hearing about new studies and pieces of research is all very well, but you must understand what it is that you are reading. It is important that you know how new theories are developed and how research is carried out.

Reliability and validity

There are specific methods of carrying out research to ensure the results are both reliable and valid. Research is judged on both of these factors, and you need to be able to satisfy yourself that the reports you read are based on reliable and valid research.

Reliability means the results would be repeated if someone else were to carry out the same piece of research in exactly the same way. **Validity** means that the conclusions that have been drawn from the research are consistent with the results, consistent with the way in which the research was carried out and consistent in the way in which the information has been interpreted.

The research process

You will need to understand some of the basic terms which are used when discussing research in any field.

- **Primary research** refers to information or data which is obtained directly from the research carried out, not from books or previously published work.
- **Secondary research** refers to information obtained from books, previously published research and reports, CD Roms, the Internet, etc. – any information which is obtained from work carried out by others. For example, if you were asked to write an assignment you are most likely to find the information from secondary sources such as textbooks or the Internet, rather than carry out a research project yourself in order to establish the information you need.

The information obtained from research is often referred to as **data**. It is called data regardless of whether it is in numbers or in words.

There are two broad areas of approach to research and they determine both the way in which the research is carried out and the type of results that are obtained. The first is referred to as **quantitative**, the second is **qualitative**.

Quantitative research

This approach has developed from the way in which scientists carry out laboratory experiments. The method produces statistical and numerical information. It provides hard facts and figures, and uses statistics and numbers to draw conclusions and make an analysis.

Many researchers in the field of health and care use quantitative approaches and produce quantitative data. They may carry out 'experiments' using many of the rules of scientific investigation. In general, if you are reading research which provides statistics and numerical information and is based purely on facts, it is likely to have used one of the quantitative approaches.

Many government publications are good examples of quantitative research – they give statistics in relation to the National Health Service, for example, such as the numbers of patients on waiting lists, the numbers having a particular operation, or the numbers of residents in nursing homes throughout the country.

Qualitative research

A qualitative approach looks at the 'quality' rather than the 'quantity' of something. It would be used to investigate the feelings of people who have remained on the waiting list for treatment, or people's attitudes towards residential care, or the relationships between those in residential care and those who care for them. Generally, qualitative data is produced in words rather than figures and will consist of descriptions and information about people's lives, experiences and attitudes.

Check it out

By using any of the methods for finding up-to-date information, such as newspapers, journals, reports, television, the Internet or textbooks, find two pieces of research carried out within the past two years. One should be quantitative and one qualitative. Read the results of both pieces of research and make a note of the differences in the type of information provided.

Carrying out research

All research begins with a **hypothesis**, which identifies what it is you intend to find out. The purpose of research is to answer questions, and a hypothesis suggests an answer to the question. The research will be carried out to test whether the hypothesis is correct. For example, if you were interested in knowing the attitudes of young people with a disability to living in adapted independent accommodation, you could start with a hypothesis and carry out some research to test it. Your hypothesis might say: 'The majority of young people with a disability wish to live independently in specially adapted accommodation.' Alternatively, you may want to find out the number of visits from friends and family to residents of a nursing home, and whether those visits decrease over time. You could start with a hypothesis which states: 'The number of visits of friends and relatives to residents of Sunnybank Nursing Home decreases after the first year of residency.' Your research would then be carried out to see whether this hypothesis was proved to be true.

Methods of investigation

Having decided on your research question and on the hypothesis you intend to test, the next stage is to choose the appropriate method of investigation. There are many ways of collecting data. It can be done through questionnaires, interviews, through observations or experiments. All of these methods require the researcher to select a sample of people to whom questionnaires can be given, with whom interviews can be carried out, who will be observed, or who can be asked to participate in experiments.

The selection of the method of investigation and the subsequent choice of sample are very important in establishing the validity and reliability of the research. Most of the criticisms of research are based on the methods used to carry out the research. It is almost impossible, particularly in the field of health and social care, to carry out research which is not affected by **variables**. These are factors which can make a difference to the final data produced, but do not have a direct relationship with it. Because this type of research involves people and their experiences, there are many factors which are variable and it can be hard to produce purely scientific, factual research.

Presenting data

The data resulting from any research can be presented in a variety of ways. Most researchers use tables and graphs to present statistical information, as in the examples below.

Month	No. of visits
January	21
February	45
March	69
April	112
May	136
June	151

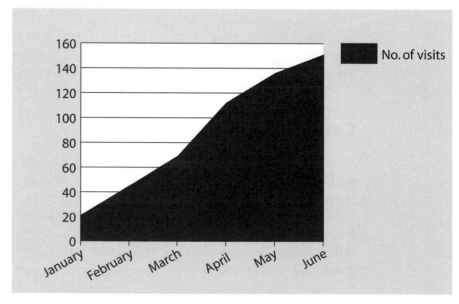

It is also possible to show data in charts and pie diagrams, as below.

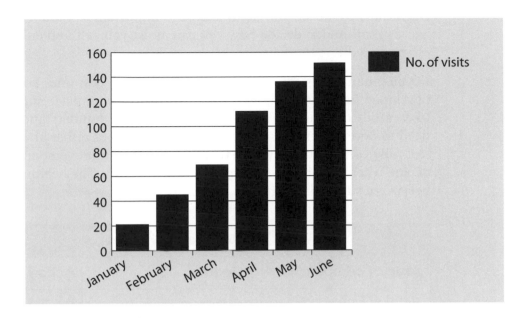

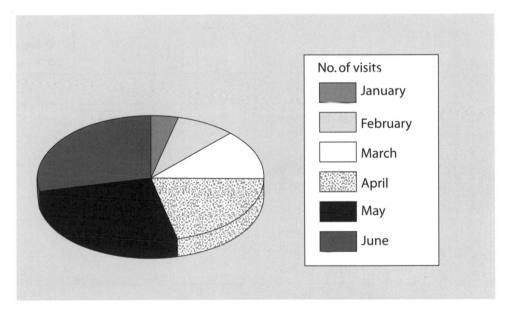

Demonstrating statistics in this visual way makes it easier for people to understand the implications of the data. However, these types of presentations must be accompanied by a detailed written report which explains the way in which the research was carried out, the results, and the implications of those results. Many large research projects can fill an entire book with their results.

Check it out

Carry out a small piece of research based on your own workplace. Decide the research question that you want to explore and then decide the way in which you will approach it. You will need to work with your supervisor on this project.

Preparing a development plan

Regardless of the job you do, it is always important to think clearly about your career goals and to decide how you can assist yourself and enlist the support of others to achieve those goals.

Development plans can take many forms, but the best ones are likely to be developed in conjunction with your manager or workplace supervisor. You need to carefully consider the 'areas of competence' and understand which ones you need to develop for your work role. Identify each as either an area in which you feel fully confident, one where there is room for improvement and development, or one where you have very limited current ability. The headings in the table below are suggestions only.

Development plan		
Area of competence	**Goals**	**Action plan**
Time management and workload organisation	Learn to use computer recording and information systems	Attend 2-day training and use study pack. Attend follow up training days. Use computer instead of writing reports by hand.
Review date: 3 months		
Professional development priorities My priorities for training and development in the next 6 months are:	IT and computerised record systems.	
My priorities for training and development in the next 6-12 months are:	As above and NVQ assessor training.	
Repeat this exercise in: 6 months and review the areas of competence and priorities.		

Once you have completed your plan you can identify the areas on which you need to concentrate. You should set some goals and targets, and your line manager should be able to help you ensure they are realistic.

For example, if you were to decide that you needed to achieve competence in managing a team in six months, this would be unrealistic and unachievable. You would inevitably fail to meet your target and would therefore be likely to become demoralised and demotivated. But if your target was to attend a training and development programme on team building during the next six months and to lead perhaps two team meetings by the end of the six months, those goals and targets would be realistic and you would be likely to achieve them.

Only you and your line manager can examine the areas of competence and skills which you need to achieve. This is a personal development programme for you and you must be sure that it reflects not only the objectives of your organisation and the job roles they may want you to fulfil, but also your personal ambitions and aspirations.

When you have identified the areas in which you feel competent and chosen your target areas for development, you will need to design a personal development log which will enable you to keep a record of your progress. This can be put together in any way that you find effective.

In your plan you may wish to include things as varied as learning sign language, learning a particular technique for working with service users with dementia, or developing your potential as a manager by learning organisational and human resources skills. You could also include areas such as time management and stress management. All of these are legitimate areas for inclusion in your personal and professional development plan.

Outcome activity 3.2

Your task is to prepare a Personal Development Plan. You should use a computer to do this, even if you print out a hard copy in order to keep a personal portfolio.

Step 1
Use the model on the following pages to prepare your plan.

Step 2
Complete the plan as far as you can at the present time. Note where you want your career to be in the short, medium and long term. You should also note down the training you want to complete and the skills you want to gain. You should do this on a computer if possible, otherwise complete a hard copy and keep it in a file.

Step 3
Update the plan regularly. Keep on reviewing it with your supervisor.

Personal development plan
Name:
Workplace:
Supervisor:
Long-term goals (1-5 years)
Medium-term goals (6-12 months)
Short-term goals (next 6 months)
Areas of strength
Areas of weakness

Training and development

This section helps you to look at what you need to do in order to reach the goals you recorded in the first section. You should make a note of the training and development you need to undertake in order to achieve what you have identified.

Short-term goals	Development needed
Medium-term goals	Development needed
Long-term goals	Development needed

Milestones and timescales

In this section you should look at the development you have identified in the previous section and plan some timescales. Decide what the 'milestones' will be on the way to achieving your goal. Make sure that your timescales are realistic.

Development	Milestone	By when

Reviews and updates

This section helps you to stay on track and to make the changes which will be inevitable as you progress. Not all your milestones will be achieved on target – some will be later, some earlier. All these changes will affect your overall plan, and you need to keep up to date and make any alterations as you go along.

Milestone	Target date	Actual achievement/ revised target

One of the most valuable roles of all team members is to share the information they have. This may be information picked up from a meeting or a training day, or it may be from a TV documentary, or information found on the Internet.

One of the important contributions that you can make to your team and to the development of all team members is to make sure that you do not keep useful information to yourself and fail to let others know about it.

There is an old but true saying that knowledge is power, and some people hold onto the information they obtain in the hope that it will give them an edge or an advantage over other people, even their own team members. Such people are not functioning well as members of a team or fulfilling the basic requirement of contributing to team effectiveness.

If there is a member in your team who has the tendency to behave in this way, the team will need to consider some strategies to deal with it. One effective way may be to suggest that at each team meeting a different team member makes a presentation which will be of value to others about some new or emerging information. After doing this, the team member who is causing difficulties should be praised and encouraged for the valuable contribution made. This should help him or her to see that there is more to be gained from sharing information with others than from keeping it to oneself.

In organisations, information and knowledge can 'cascade' to others.

But there is little point in sharing information with your colleagues unless you do it in a way that they can understand and accept. Pinning an interesting article on a notice board may be one way of allowing people to see it, but people don't always notice what is on a board, nor is it easy to stand and read a whole article in this way. If you would like to share an interesting article with team members, the most useful thing is probably to ask your manager if you can photocopy the article and distribute it.

If you have been to a particularly valuable meeting or training day, you may want to copy and share any notes or handouts with your colleagues, or it may be possible for you to give a short presentation at a team meeting. This is called **cascading**, and it is used by many organisations as a cost-effective way of sharing information gained from training or conferences across a wide range of staff.

Check it out

Think of an occasion when some useful or interesting information was passed on to you by a fellow team member. How did it make you feel?

Making good use of training/development opportunities

All members of a team will benefit from understanding how to make the most of opportunities for training and development, and the many different ways of developing, both as an individual and as a professional care worker.

Personal development is to do with developing the personal qualities and skills that everyone needs in order to live and work with others, such as understanding, empathy, patience, communication and relationship-building. It is also to do with the development of self-confidence, self-esteem and self-respect. If you look back on the ways in which you have changed over the past five years, you are likely to find that you are different in quite a few ways. Most people change as they mature and gain more life experience. Important experiences such as changing jobs, moving home, illness or bereavement can change people.

It is inevitable that personal development and professional development are linked – your personality and the way you relate to others are the major tools you use to do your job. Taking advantage of every opportunity to train and develop your working skills will also have an impact on you as a person.

The skills you need for work must be regularly updated, so you should take advantage of any opportunity to learn something new.

Professional development is to do with developing the qualities and skills that are necessary for the workplace. Example are teamwork, the ability to communicate with different types of people, time management, organisation, problem solving, decision making and, of course, the skills specific to the job.

Continuous professional development involves regularly updating the skills you need for work. You can achieve this through attending training sessions both on- and off-the-job, and by making the most of the opportunities you have for training by careful planning and preparation.

How to get the best out of training

Team managers and supervisors will work with a team to decide on the types of training each individual will benefit from most. This will be different depending on the stage each person has reached in skills and experience. There would be little point, for example, in sending someone on a course in micro-surgery techniques if he or she was at the stage of having just achieved a First Aid certificate! It may be that not all the training team members want to do is appropriate for the work the team is currently doing – a course in advanced therapeutic activities may sound fascinating, but the team supervisor may suggest that a course in basic moving and handling techniques is what is needed right now. People will only get the best out of training and development opportunities if they are the right ones at the right time. There will be opportunities for training throughout everyone's career, and it is important to work out which training is going to help to achieve the goals which have been set.

Stress

All of us know someone who appears to cope with demands and a work load that most of us would simply be unable to manage, yet seems to thrive in what could be an extremely stressful situation. Responses to stress are individual and so are, to a large extent, the effects.

Stress can show itself in a number of ways. Emotionally, stress can cause people to feel:

▶ tense, irritable, angry
▶ depressed, anxious, tearful, worthless
▶ unable to cope, to concentrate or make decisions
▶ tired and stretched to the limit
▶ uninterested in everything, including sex.

Physically, stress can cause:

▶ tensing of the muscles
▶ headaches, migraines
▶ circulatory disorders such as high blood pressure, heart attacks, strokes
▶ respiratory disorders such as asthma and chest pains
▶ digestive disorders such as ulcers
▶ menstrual problems
▶ increases in infections, such as cold sores and colds.

What causes stress?

Stress means different things to different people. The kinds of things that can cause stress include:

▶ work pressures
▶ being in debt

- having relationship problems
- interrupted sleep.

Stress is believed to be one of the major causes of time off work and of staff turnover. Stress at work can be caused by:

- poor working relationships
- the type of work that has to be carried out, especially in social care
- the hours spent at work, especially for shift workers
- a lack of career progression opportunities
- a fear of redundancy or retirement.

Check it out

Think of an occasion when you felt very stressed. Make a list of the feelings/emotions and physical symptoms you had at the time.

Methods of dealing with stress

Everyone has their own way of coping with stress, but sometimes people's coping mechanisms can make the situation worse! Things to avoid are:

- drinking alcohol
- smoking
- compulsive eating.

Behaviours like these might make people feel better at the time, but in the long run can be very damaging to health.

Positive ways to deal with stress include the following.

- Physical activity, for example going for a walk, doing some gardening, even punching a pillow. Physical activity uses up the extra energy our bodies produce when stressed.
- Talking things over, for example with a friend or supervisor. Chatting about a problem often helps people identify the real issues and how to deal with them.
- Doing something to take your mind off the problem, for example going to the cinema or reading a magazine. Escaping from a problem for a while enables you to come back to it with a clear head, and feel more able to tackle things.
- Using relaxation techniques – activities in which you learn to control your breathing. These can help to release the muscular tension that goes hand-in-hand with stress.
- Organising your time well. Don't take on more than you can handle, and do things in order of their importance.
- Learning to shrug things off. Raise your shoulders and lower them a few times. This uses up energy, leaving you feeling more relaxed; it also helps you get things into perspective. How important is what is causing the stress anyway?

Anyone suffering from symptoms of stress which persist, and who can see no way forward, should seek help.

Support, advice and guidance

Family and friends are usually the first people to look to for support. They have either experienced stress themselves or know someone who has been in that position, and can offer support and help.

If stress is associated with work, talking things through with a supervisor should help. Some organisations employ individuals whose role includes counselling people with problems and guiding them in finding solutions. Often stressful situations at work can be improved by learning to manage time more effectively, or how to be more assertive so that it is easier to refuse to take on excessive work, or to deal with situations in which people feel they have no control.

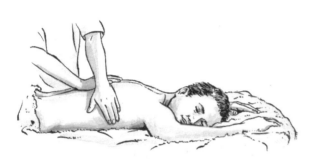

If the symptoms of stress are seriously affecting your life, or if they have gone on for a long time, you should see your GP, who could treat your physical symptoms and perhaps refer you to a suitably qualified therapist or counsellor.

Massage or alternative therapies such as reflexology and aromatherapy can also be very valuable in helping to relieve stress.

There are also voluntary organisations and telephone help-lines that you can contact; and a mass of literature, from leaflets through to textbooks, is available in your local library or bookshop, full of information about how to cope with stress.

Offering support to others

Supporting a work colleague in a team could mean:

▶ telling colleagues information you have discovered or something you have seen or read which would be of interest to them
▶ making sure colleagues know of opportunities for training courses which you think are likely to interest them
▶ recognising and acknowledging when a colleague has worked particularly well
▶ recognising when someone is having difficulty in a particular area of work
▶ recognising when someone is having difficulty in his or her personal life and this may be affecting work
▶ noticing when people are overloaded with work and offering to lend a hand
▶ noticing when a colleague is nervous or unsure about a new task or procedure and offering help and encouragement

▶ noticing if a colleague is being made uncomfortable by the way in which he or she is being spoken to or treated by another colleague or service user, and offering to help if needed.

If you do these things you will be making a good contribution towards the support and development of members of your team. If your team is working well, your colleagues will be doing the same thing for you, and supporting you in your development.

Check it out

Keep a calendar for a week, two weeks or even a month. Each day draw a stick figure which represents yourself, and at the end of each working shift draw arrows outwards from this figure to show how much support you have given to others in your team. Draw inward arrows for occasions when support has been offered to you. None of the examples of support needs to be large, but a series of small actions of support are most likely to contribute effectively to successful teams.

At the end of each week count up the arrows going inwards and the arrows going outwards. They should be in proportion to the people who work on the team, and you should be giving and receiving support in equal measure. If there are more arrows in than out, you need to explore additional ways in which you can support colleagues. If there are more arrows out than in, you could place your concerns on the agenda at a team meeting.

Ways to offer support

Support offered to fellow team members can sometimes be misinterpreted, so you need to ensure that you use all your communication skills in order to offer support, advice or encouragement in a way which is not seen as patronising or implying some kind of criticism of your colleague.

Every team is different in nature; some are quite formal in their relationships, whereas others are very casual and relaxed. The communication style of your team should always be taken into account in the approach you use when offering support to colleagues. If your team works on a casual, friendly basis and you notice a colleague struggling, it would be normal practice to say cheerfully: 'Want a hand?' However, if your team has more formal relationships and is not so relaxed, or if lines of responsibility and seniority are carefully observed, the same offer of help would be approached differently. Perhaps you could say: 'You look busy, Mrs Morgan, can I help with that?' The way in which help is offered can often be the key to whether or not it is accepted.

There are many situations where a colleague may be grateful for a helping hand.

If you are offering advice, support or information with a genuine desire to assist your colleagues, however, then you are unlikely to offend.

Resolving issues and difficulties

You need to work out how you will deal with any problem relationships within your team. There will inevitably be individuals in any team who do not get on well with each other. Bear in mind that a working relationship does not require the same commitment, sharing of ideals, values and understanding as a personal friendship. In order to work well with someone it is sufficient that you recognise and value his or her contribution to the team's performance, and that you always communicate effectively and courteously when working. It is not necessary that you socialise with your work colleagues, although many teams do socialise together. The loyalty and camaraderie which is built up among members of a good team can be based purely on their performance at work, and does not necessarily have to carry over into their personal lives.

Checklist: thinking positively

If you have to work with people with whom you feel you have little in common, try the following in order to view them in a more positive light.

1 List all the positive things about your colleague. For example, does he or she:

- have a nice smile?
- interact very well with the service users?
- have a particular skill in one area of practice?
- handle a crisis well?
- always try to accommodate swaps in rotas?
- have good organisational skills?
- make good coffee?

2 Make a positive comment to your colleague at least once each day. This could range from 'Your hair looks nice today' to 'I have learned such a lot from watching you deal with Mrs X'.

3 Ask questions about your colleague and try to find out more about him or her. This does not have to be on a personal level – questions could be about professional skills. You could try something like 'Where did you learn to move patients so well?' Or take the trouble to find his or her opinions on current issues. Perhaps you could ask, 'What do you think about the new set of proposals for the shift rotas?'

4 Pick up on any comments which may lead to areas of common interest. For example, your colleague may comment about something he or she has done over the weekend, or make a reference to reading something or seeing a film or a play that you know something about. You should follow up on any of these potential leads which may allow you to find out more about the individual.

5 Learn what you can about your colleagues, either by listening to others or by asking questions about the person's background and looking at where his or her ideas and influences have come from. If you understand someone's culture, beliefs and values it will be easier to see how and why he or she holds particular views and opinions.

6 Make a list of the positives that this colleague brings to the team.

Check it out

Set out an action plan of how you will tackle issues raised by those team members that you find it more difficult to relate to. You may decide that you will concentrate on looking at the quality of their work and appreciating and valuing their contribution, or you may consider their personal circumstances and develop an understanding of why they may act as they do.

If your team has reached the stage where you feel confident enough to openly share your concerns about the behaviour of another, then do so In a team meeting, provided that you can do it in a constructive way.

Be careful, before you share views about somebody's personal behaviour, that you are not making statements which are hurtful and destructive. Make sure that any aspects of behaviour that you challenge are behaviour which genuinely affects the quality of work or functioning of the team. You do not have a right to challenge someone's behaviour simply because you personally dislike it. You should challenge behaviour only if it is proving damaging towards others or the team.

Challenging inappropriate practice

You may have to deal with the situation where one of your colleagues is behaving in an inappropriate way towards service users or other care workers.

As we saw in Unit 1, Outcome 5, unacceptable behaviour by care workers can take various forms, such as:

▶ speaking about service users in a derogatory way
▶ speaking to service users in a rude or dismissive way
▶ humiliating service users
▶ undermining people's self-esteem and confidence
▶ bullying or intimidation
▶ patronising and talking down to people
▶ removing people's right to exercise choice
▶ failing to recognise and treat people as individuals
▶ not respecting people's culture, values and beliefs.

A care worker who fails to remember that all people are individuals, and all have a right to be valued and accepted, is in danger of behaving inappropriately towards service users.

Check it out

Find out from your supervisor about the ways in which inapropriate practice is dealt with in your workplace.

If you are faced with the situation where a colleague is behaving inappropriately or bad practice is being allowed to occur, you can respond in several ways. Depending on the severity of the problem, you should:

▶ challenge the behaviour, or the source of the bad practice
▶ have a one-to-one discussion with the colleague in question
▶ act as a mentor with whom your colleague can share problems and difficulties
▶ act as a role model of good practice.

Motivation

One of the factors which is likely to maintain the motivation and therefore the performance of a team is shared responsibility. Responsibility for the outcome of the team's work is often a very important factor in motivating the team. Developing challenges and plans for their own team and being responsible for the outcome, rather than handing over responsibility to management, is likely to provide team members with the challenge and motivation necessary to maintain good performance.

In order for your team to be able to accept responsibility for its actions, it will also need to have the authority to carry out the plans it has made. The team may need to approach management in order to gain this authority, and it may only be for specific events or plans that this is possible, but all the research into effective teams shows that those that have both responsibility and the authority to carry out their plans tend to maintain motivation over longer periods of time.

Outcome activity 3.3

This task involves working with at least two other people; you can work with up to six others, but this task cannot be achieved alone.

Your task is to design and produce a Development Directory for your workplace. The directory must be prepared using a word-processing, spreadsheet or graphics program, and can be available in hard copy, on-line or both. The directory will enable members of staff to find out about opportunities for training, and ways of using supervision and appraisal for their personal development. The directory should include:

▶ information about relevant training courses and conferences available locally
▶ information about how to make the most of supervision, and places to look for feedback on practice
▶ information about ways to share knowledge gained from training and development opportunities.

Step 1
Work out in your group all the different tasks involved in producing the directory. First, you may want to consider asking people what they want from a directory. You will need to decide on the format – hard copy or on-line; the research will need to be carried out; and finally the information you have gathered will have to be designed and entered into the computer. No doubt you will find other tasks during your discussions.

Step 2
Plan how you will achieve the production of the directory. You may decide to have particular people undertaking specific roles – such as organising, finding the resources, etc.; or you may decide that everyone will work together on the tasks.

Step 3
Follow your plans to produce the guide. Make sure that you have included all of the required information; you should also include anything else which you think may be relevant in your local area.

Step 4
Review the process of producing the directory. Your group should consider and answer the following questions:

1 How did your group reach decisions?
2 Was there a leader of the group?
3 Did any other roles emerge?
4 How did you resolve disagreements?
5 How did you share information?
6 How did you maintain progress on the directory?
7 At what point did your group become a team?

Health and safety within the care environment

This unit is about how you can contribute to making your workplace a safe, secure and healthy place for people who need care. In the first outcome you will learn about what needs to be done to ensure high standards of safety in a care environment. The second outcome is about how to respond in an emergency.

Outcome 1: ## Promote health and safety standards in a care environment

The legal framework

The settings in which you provide care are generally covered by the Health and Safety at Work Act 1974 (HASAWA). This Act has been updated and supplemented by many sets of regulations and guidelines, which extend it, support it or explain it.

The effect of the laws

There are many regulations, laws and guidelines dealing with health and safety. You do not need to know the detail, but you do need to know where your responsibilities begin and end.

The laws place certain responsibilities on both employers and employees. For example, it is up to the employer to provide a safe place in which to work, but the employee also has to show reasonable care for his or her own safety.

Employers have to:

▶ provide a safe workplace
▶ ensure that there is safe access to and from the workplace
▶ provide information on health and safety
▶ provide health and safety training
▶ undertake risk assessment for all hazards.

Workers must:

▶ take reasonable care for their own safety and that of others
▶ co-operate with the employer in respect of health and safety matters
▶ not intentionally damage any health and safety equipment or materials provided by the employer.

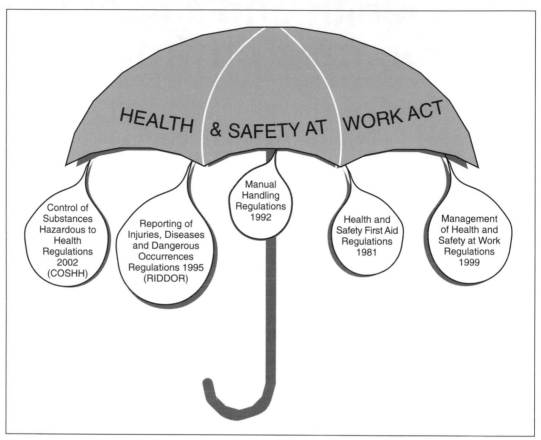

The Health and Safety at Work Act is like an umbrella.

Both the employee and employer are jointly responsible for safeguarding the health and safety of anyone using the premises. Any hazards you come across should be reported to your supervisor immediately so that steps can be taken promptly. Each workplace will have its own reporting system for hazards identified by staff. This can be as simple as telling a senior member of staff, or it may mean recording it in some way so that it can be passed on. Make sure that you know the procedure for reporting hazards in your workplace.

Each workplace where there are five or more workers must have a written statement of health and safety policy. The policy must include:

- ▶ a statement of intention to provide a safe workplace
- ▶ the name of the person responsible for implementing the policy
- ▶ the names of any other individuals responsible for particular health and safety hazards
- ▶ a list of identified health and safety hazards and the procedures to be followed in relation to them
- ▶ procedures for recording accidents at work
- ▶ details for evacuation of the premises.

Check it out

Find out where the health and safety policy is for your workplace and make sure you read it.

Safe storage of hazardous substances

Healthy lifestyles and healthy workplaces also depend on the safe use and storage of cleaning materials, and other potentially hazardous substances. What are hazardous substances? The Control of Substances Hazardous to Health (COSHH) Regulations apply to substances which are toxic, corrosive or irritant. This includes cleaning materials, pesticides, acids, disinfectants and bleaches, and naturally occurring substances such as blood, bacteria, etc. Workplaces may have other hazardous substances which are particular to the nature of the work carried out.

Employers must take the following steps to protect employees from hazardous substances:

▶ Find out what hazardous substances are used in the workplace and the risks these substances pose to people's health.
▶ Decide what precautions are needed before any work starts with hazardous substances.
▶ Prevent people from being exposed to hazardous substances, but where this is not reasonably practicable, control the exposure.
▶ Make sure control measures are used and maintained properly, and that safety procedures are followed.
▶ If required, monitor exposure of employees to hazardous substances.
▶ Carry out health surveillance where assessment has shown that this is necessary, or COSHH makes specific requirements.
▶ If required, prepare plans and procedures to deal with accidents, incidents and emergencies.
▶ Make sure employees are properly informed, trained and supervised.

The COSHH file

Every workplace must have a COSHH file. This file lists all the hazardous substances used in the workplace. It should detail:

▶ where they are kept
▶ how they are labelled
▶ their effects
▶ the maximum amount of time it is safe to be exposed to them
▶ how to deal with an emergency involving one of them.

Check it out

Ask to see the COSHH file in your workplace. Make sure you read it and know which substances you use or come into contact with. Check in the file what the maximum exposure limits are. Your employer must include this information in the COSHH file.

If you have to work with hazardous substances, which may be cleaning or other materials, make sure that you take the precautions detailed in the COSHH file – this may mean wearing gloves or protective goggles, or it may involve limiting the time you are exposed to the substance or only using it in certain circumstances.

The COSHH file should also give you information about how to store hazardous substances. This will involve using the correct containers as supplied by the manufacturers. All containers must have safety lids and caps, and must be correctly labelled.

Never use the container of one substance for storing another, and *never* change the labels.

These symbols, which warn you of hazardous substances, are always yellow.

The symbols above indicate hazardous substances. They are there for your safety and the safety of those you care for. Before you use *any* substance, whether it is liquid, powder, spray, cream or aerosol, take the following simple steps:

▶ Check the container for the hazard symbol.
▶ If there is a hazard symbol, go to the COSHH file.
▶ Look up the precautions you need to take with the substance.
▶ Make sure you follow the procedures, which are intended to protect you.

If you are concerned that a substance being used in your workplace is not in the COSHH file, or if you notice incorrect containers or labels being used, report it to your supervisor. Once you have informed your supervisor, it becomes his or her responsibility to act to correct the problem.

Reporting problems

In your workplace, you have a responsibility to report any unsafe situation to your employer. For example, if you come to use a piece of equipment – anything from a hoist to a kettle – and find that it is unsafe or needs repair, you must report it. It is not enough to assume that someone else will notice it, or to say 'It's not up to me – that's a manager's job'. You have a share in the responsibility of making your workplace safe and secure.

However, there are some other situations which have to reported officially, not just to your employer, and there are special procedures to be followed.

Reporting of Injuries, Diseases and Dangerous Occurrences (RIDDOR)

Reporting accidents and ill-health at work is a legal requirement. All accidents, diseases and dangerous occurrences should be reported to the Incident Contact Centre. The Contact Centre was established on 1 April 2001 as a single point of contact for all incidents in the UK. The information is important because it means that risks and causes of accidents, incidents and diseases can be identified. All notifications are passed on to either the local authority Environmental Health department, or the Health and Safety Executive, as appropriate.

Your employer needs to report:

- deaths
- major injuries (see below)
- accidents resulting in more than three days off work
- diseases
- dangerous occurrences.

Reportable major injuries and diseases

The following injuries need to be reported:

- fracture other than to fingers, thumbs or toes
- amputation
- dislocation of the shoulder, hip, knee or spine
- loss of sight (temporary or permanent)
- chemical or hot metal burn to the eye or any penetrating injury to the eye
- injury resulting from an electric shock or electrical burn leading to unconsciousness or requiring resuscitation or admittance to hospital for more than 24 hours

- any other injury which leads to hypothermia (getting too cold), heat-induced illness, or unconsciousness; requires resuscitation; or requires admittance to hospital for more than 24 hours
- unconsciousness caused by asphyxia (suffocation) or exposure to a harmful substance or biological agent
- acute illness requiring medical treatment, or leading to loss of consciousness, arising from absorption of any substance by inhalation, ingestion or through the skin
- acute illness requiring medical treatment where there is reason to believe that this resulted from exposure to a biological agent or its toxins or infected material.

Reportable diseases include:

- certain poisonings
- some skin diseases such as occupational dermatitis, skin cancer, chrome ulcer, oil folliculitis acne
- lung diseases including: occupational asthma, farmer's lung, pneumoconiosis, asbestosis, mesothelioma
- infections such as: leptospirosis, hepatitis, tuberculosis, anthrax, legionellosis (Legionnaires' disease) and tetanus
- other conditions such as: occupational cancer, certain musculoskeletal disorders, decompression illness and hand-arm vibration syndrome.

Dangerous occurrences

If something happens which does not result in a reportable injury, but which clearly could have done, then it may be a dangerous occurrence which must be reported immediately.

If someone slips on a wet floor, you must record the incident.

Accidents at work

If accidents or injuries occur at work, either to you or to an individual you are caring for, then the details must be recorded. For example, someone may have a fall, or slip on a wet floor. You must record the incident regardless of whether there was an injury.

Your employer should have procedures in place for making a record of accidents, either an accident book or an accident report form. This is not only required by the RIDDOR regulations, but also, if you work in a residential or nursing home, by the Care Standards Commission.

Make sure you know where the accident report forms or the accident book are kept, and who is responsible for recording accidents. It is likely to be your manager.

You must report any accident in which you are involved, or that you have witnessed, to your manager or supervisor.

Any medical treatment or assessment which is necessary should be arranged without delay. If an individual has been involved in an accident, you should check if there is anyone he or she would like to be contacted, perhaps a relative or friend. If the accident is serious, and you cannot consult the individual – because he or she is unconscious, for example – the next of kin should be informed as soon as possible.

Complete a report, and ensure that all witnesses to the accident also complete reports. You should include the following in any accident report (see the example below):

▶ date, time and place of accident
▶ person/people involved
▶ circumstances and details of exactly what you saw
▶ anything which was said by the individuals involved
▶ the condition of the individual after the accident
▶ steps taken to summon help, time of summoning help and time when help arrived
▶ names of any other people who witnessed the accident
▶ any equipment involved in the accident.

Date: 24.3.04   **Time:** 14.30 hrs   **Location:** Main lounge

Description of accident:
PH got out of her chair and began to walk across the lounge with the aid of her stick. She turned her head to continue the conversation she had been having with GK, and as she turned back again she appeared not to have noticed that MP's handbag had been left on the floor. PH tripped over handbag and fell heavily, banging her head on a footstool.

She was very shaken and although she said that she was not hurt, there was a large bump on her head. P appeared pale and shaky. I asked J to fetch a blanket and to call Mrs J, deputy officer in charge. Covered P with a blanket. Mrs J arrived immediately. Dr was sent for after P was examined by Mrs J.

Dr arrived after about 20 mins and said that she was bruised and shaken, but did not seem to have any injuries.

She wanted to go and lie down. She was helped to bed.

Incident was witnessed by six residents who were in the lounge at the time: GK, MP, IL, MC, CR and BQ.

Signed   Name:

-        - - - - - - - - - - - - - -

An example of an accident report.

Check it out

Your manager has asked you to design a new incident/accident report form for your workplace. She has asked you to do this because the current form does not provide enough information. The purpose of the new form is to provide sufficient information to:

▶ ensure the individual receives the proper medical attention
▶ provide information for treatment at a later date, in case of delayed reactions
▶ give information to any inspector who may need to see the records
▶ identify any gaps or need for improvements in safety procedures
▶ provide information about the circumstances in case of any future legal action.

Think about how you would design the new report form and what headings you would include. Use the list above as a checklist to make sure you have covered everything you need.

Manual handling

One of the commonest causes of accidents to care workers, and often to service users, is the process of moving people around when they need assistance.

DID YOU KNOW?

Lifting and handling individuals is the single largest cause of injuries at work in health and care settings. One in four workers takes time off because of a back injury sustained at work.

The Manual Handling Operations Regulations 1992 require employers to avoid all manual handling where there is a risk of injury 'so far as it is reasonably practical'. Everyone from the European Commission to the Royal College of Nurses has issued policies and directives about avoiding lifting, but these have been the subject of legal challenge (see the next page). Make sure you check out the policies in use in your workplace and that you understand them.

There is almost no situation in which manual lifting and handling could be considered acceptable, but the views and rights of the service user being lifted must be taken into account and a balance achieved.

REMEMBER

▶ Always use lifting and handling aids.
▶ There is no such thing as a safe lift.
▶ Use the aids which your employer is obliged to provide.

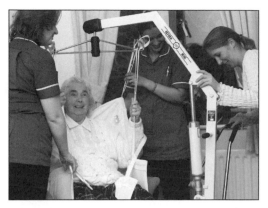

Lifting should be done with the appropriate aids and sufficient people.

On the rare occasions when it is still absolutely necessary for manual lifting to be done, the employer has to make a 'risk assessment' and put procedures in place to reduce the risk of injury to the employee. This could involve ensuring that sufficient staff are available to lift or handle someone safely, which can often mean that four people are needed.

All lifting and handling should be carried out using appropriate aids and sufficient people. Manual lifting is not something to be undertaken in the normal course of events and you should use mechanical lifting aids and hoists wherever possible.

REMEMBER

Your employer has a statutory duty to install lifting equipment, but it is your responsibility to use the equipment that is there.

If you do have to lift, what should you do?

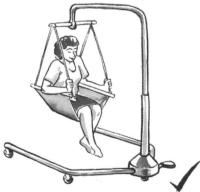

Use the aids which your employer is obliged to provide.

Encourage all individuals to help themselves – you would be surprised how much 'learned helplessness' exists. This is largely brought about by care workers who find it is quicker and easier to do things themselves rather than allowing a person to do it for himself or herself!

It is also essential that the views of the person being moved are taken into account. While you and your employer need to make sure that you are not put at risk by moving or lifting, it is also important that the person needing assistance is not caused pain, distress or humiliation. Groups representing disabled people have pointed out that blanket policies which exclude any lifting may infringe the human rights of an individual needing mobility assistance. For example, individuals may in effect be confined to bed unnecessarily and against their will by a lack of lifting assistance. A High Court judgement (A & B vs East Sussex County Council, 2003) found in favour of two disabled women who had been denied access to lifting because the local authority had a 'blanket ban' on lifting regardless of circumstances. Such a ban was deemed unlawful. It is likely that similar cases will be brought under the Human Rights Act, which gives people protection against humiliating or degrading treatment.

REMEMBER

▶ Many workers in care still lift people manually. It seems quicker and easier than going to all the trouble of using a hoist – it isn't.

▶ Manual lifting is now actively discouraged throughout the profession.

▶ Manual lifting usually presents unnecessary and unacceptable risks to the service user and to you.

▶ The wishes of a service user must be taken into account.

▶ A back injury can end your career. It's not worth the risk.

Your employer should arrange for you to attend a lifting and handling course. You must attend one each year, so that you are up to date with the safest possible practices.

How to maintain security

Most workplaces where care is provided are not under lock and key. This is an inevitable part of ensuring that people have choice and that their rights are respected. However, they also have a right to be secure. Security in a care environment is about:

▶ security against intruders

▶ security in respect of their privacy and decisions about unwanted visitors

▶ security against being abused

▶ security of property.

Security against intruders

If you work for a large organisation, such as an NHS trust, it may be that all employees are easily identifiable by identity badges with photographs. This makes it easier to spot people who do not have a right to be on the premises.

In a smaller workplace, there may be a system of issuing visitors' badges to visitors who have reasons to be there, or it may simply rely on the vigilance of the staff.

Some workplaces operate electronic security systems, like those in the NHS where cards are 'swiped' to open doors. Less sophisticated systems in smaller workplaces may use a keypad with a code number known only to staff and those who are legitimately on the premises. It is often difficult to maintain security with such systems, as codes are forgotten or become widely known. In order to maintain security, it is necessary to change the codes regularly, and to make sure everyone is aware.

Some workplaces still operate with keys, although the days of staff walking about with large bunches of keys attached to a belt are fast disappearing. If mechanical keys are used, there will be a list of named keyholders and there is likely to be a system of handover of keys at shift change. However, each workplace has its own system and you need to be sure that you understand which security system operates in your workplace.

Keys to good practice

✔ Be aware of everyone you come across. Get into the habit of noticing people and thinking, 'Do I know that person?'
✔ Challenge anyone you do not recognise.
✔ The challenge should be polite. 'Can I help you?' is usually enough to find out if a visitor has a reason to be on the premises.

If a person says that he or she is there to see someone:

✔ Don't give directions – escort him or her.
✔ If the person is a genuine visitor, he or she will be grateful. If not, he or she will disappear pretty quickly!

The more dependent individuals are, the greater the risk. If you work with babies, high-dependency or unconscious patients, people with a severe learning disability or multiple disabilities or people who are very confused, you will have to be extremely vigilant in protecting them from criminals. Workplaces where most or all service users are in individual rooms can also be difficult to make secure, as it is not always possible to check every room if service users choose to close the door. A routine check can be very time consuming, and can affect service users' rights to privacy and dignity.

Communal areas are easier to check, but can present their own problems; it can be difficult to be sure who is a legitimate visitor and who should not be there. Some establishments provide all visitors with badges, but while this may be acceptable in a large institution or an office block, it is not compatible with creating a comfortable and relaxed atmosphere in a residential setting. Extra care must be taken to check that you know all the people in a communal area. If you are not sure, ask. It is better to risk offending someone by asking 'Can I help you?' or 'Are you waiting for someone?' than to leave an intruder unchallenged.

REMEMBER

If you find an intruder on the premises, don't tackle him or her – raise the alarm.

Protecting people

If very dependent individuals are living in their own homes, the risks are far greater. You must try to impress on them the importance of finding out who people are before letting them in. If they are able to use it, the 'password' scheme from the utilities (water, gas and electricity companies) is helpful. Information record cards like those provided by the 'Safe as Houses' scheme can be invaluable in providing basic information to anyone who is involved in helping in an emergency.

REMEMBER

- Every time you visit, you may have to explain again what the individual should do when someone knocks on the door.
- Give the individual a card with simple instructions.
- Obtain agreement to speak to the local 'homewatch' scheme and ask that a special eye is kept on visitors.
- Speak to the local police and make them aware that a vulnerable individual is living alone in the house.

Security of property

Property and valuables belonging to individuals in care settings should be safeguarded. It is likely that your employer will have a property book in which records of all valuables and personal possessions are entered.

There may be particular policies within your organisation, but as a general rule you are likely to need to:

- make a record of all possessions on admission
- record valuable items separately
- describe items of jewellery by their colour, for example 'yellow metal' not 'gold'
- ensure that individuals sign for any valuables they are keeping, and that they understand that they are liable for their loss
- inform your manager if an individual is keeping valuables or a significant amount of money.

Check it out

Find out where the property book is in your workplace, and how it is filled in. Check who has the responsibility to complete it. If you are likely to have to use the book at any time, make sure you know exactly what your role is. Do you have to enter the property in the book, then give it to someone else to deal with the valuables? Do you have to make sure the valuables are safe? Do you have to give the individual a copy of the entry in the book? Ask the questions in advance – don't leave it until you have to do it.

It is always difficult when items go missing in a care setting, particularly if they are valuable. It is important that you check all possibilities before calling the police.

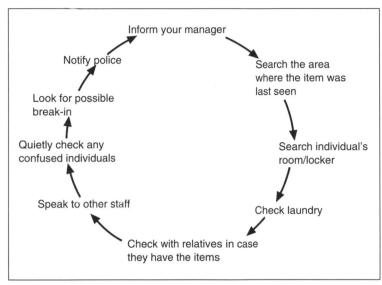

Action stages when property goes missing.

Restricting access

People have a right to choose whom they see. This can often be a difficult area to deal with. If there are relatives or friends who wish to visit and an individual does not want to see them, you may have to make this clear. It is difficult to do, but you can only be effective if you are clear and assertive. You should not make excuses or invent reasons why visitors cannot see the person concerned. You could say something like: 'I'm sorry, Mr P has told us that he does not want to see you. I understand that this may be upsetting, but it is his choice. If he does change his mind we will contact you. Would you like to leave your phone number?'

Do not allow yourself to be drawn into passing on messages or attempting to persuade – that is not your role. Your job is to respect the wishes of the person you are caring for. If you are asked to intervene or to pass on a message, you must refuse politely but firmly: 'I'm sorry, that is not something I can do. If your uncle does decide he wants to see you, I will let you know right away. I will tell him you have visited, but I can't do anything else.'

There may also be occasions when access is restricted for other reasons; possibly because someone is seriously ill and there are medical reasons for limiting access, or because of a legal restriction such as court order. In either case, it should be clearly recorded on the service user's record and your supervisor will advise you about the restrictions.

Outside the usual care setting

There are always additional health and safety considerations when you are providing care or support to service users outside the normal environment. For example, if you are planning a visit or holiday trip, you may need to consider the following:

▶ accessibility
▶ safety of premises and potential hazards
▶ accessibility and safety of transport
▶ provision of safe toilet facilities
▶ security of people, property and travel documents
▶ safety checks on any equipment
▶ instructions for using any unfamiliar equipment
▶ provision for special dietary arrangements
▶ insurance.

A change in environment can prove unsettling for some service users, and extra vigilance may be needed to ensure that vulnerable people are not distressed by the changes.

Outcome activity 5.1

This activity should be based on your own workplace if possible. If not, you could use any other suitable establishment. You could work on your own, or in a small group.

Step 1
Draw a plan to scale of your workplace showing at least three rooms, the entrance and at least one emergency escape route other than the main entrance. Show the reception area if there is one, all the doorways and windows. If you have access to a suitable computer program, and the necessary skills, use IT to produce your plan.

Step 2
Mark on your plan all the fire extinguishers and/or fire blankets available.

Mark any security checking systems on doors or in the reception area.

Clearly show emergency escape routes.

Identify any potential hazards.

Step 3
Make notes, either on the plan or using a key to the plan, about:

▶ the types of fire extinguisher in each location and why they are appropriate
▶ how the security checking systems operate and why they are needed
▶ how an emergency evacuation would be undertaken
▶ what the hazards are and how they should be assessed.

Step 4
Present your findings and your plan to your tutor.

This outcome is about first aid, and helping you to understand the actions you should take if a health emergency arises. This is not a substitute for a first aid course, and will give you only an outline of the steps you need to take. You cannot become qualified to deal with these emergencies by studying a book. Unless you have been trained on a first aid course, you should be careful about what you do, because the wrong action can cause more harm to a casualty. It is always best to summon help.

What you can safely do

Most people have a useful role to play in a health emergency, even if it is not dealing directly with the ill or injured person. It is also vital that someone:

▶ summons help as quickly as possible
▶ offers assistance to the competent person who is dealing with the emergency
▶ clears the immediate environment and makes it safe – for example, if someone has fallen through a glass door, the glass must be removed as soon as possible before there are any more injuries
▶ offers help and support to other people who have witnessed the illness or injury and may have been upset by it. Clearly this can only be dealt with once the ill or injured person is being helped.

REMEMBER

Only attempt what you know you can safely do. Do not attempt something you are not sure of. You could do further damage to the ill or injured person and you could lay yourself and your employer open to being sued. Do not try to do something outside your responsibility or capability – summon help and wait for it to arrive.

How you can help the casualty in a health emergency

It is important that you are aware of the initial steps to take when dealing with the commonest health emergencies. You may be involved with any of these emergencies when you are at work, whether you work in a residential, hospital or community setting. Clearly, there are major differences between the different work situations.

▶ If you are working in a hospital where skilled assistance is always immediately available, the likelihood of your having to act in an emergency, other than to summon help, is remote.
▶ In a residential setting, help is likely to be readily available, although it may not necessarily be the professional medical expertise of a hospital.

- In the community you may have to summon help and take action to support a casualty until the help arrives. It is in this setting that you are most likely to need some knowledge of how to respond to a health emergency.

This section gives a guide to recognising and taking initial action in a number of health emergencies:

- severe bleeding
- cardiac arrest
- shock
- loss of consciousness
- epileptic seizure
- choking and difficulty with breathing
- fractures and suspected fractures
- burns and scalds
- poisoning
- electrical injuries.

Severe bleeding

Severe bleeding can be the result of a fall or injury. The most common causes of severe cuts are glass, as the result of a fall into a window or glass door, or knives from accidents in the kitchen.

Symptoms

There will be apparently large quantities of blood from the wound. In some very serious cases, the blood may be pumping out. Even small amounts of blood can be very frightening, both for you and the casualty. Remember that a small amount of blood goes a long way, and things may look worse than they are. However, severe bleeding requires urgent medical attention in hospital. Although people rarely bleed to death, extensive bleeding can cause shock and loss of consciousness.

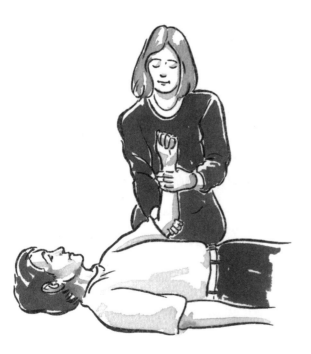

Lay the casualty down and raise the affected part.

Aims

- To bring the bleeding under control
- To limit the possibility of infection
- To arrange urgent medical attention

Action

1 You will need to apply pressure to a wound that is bleeding. If possible, use a sterile dressing. If one is not readily available, use

any absorbent material, or even your hand. Do not forget the precautions (see 'Protect yourself' below). You will need to apply direct pressure over the wound for 10 minutes (this can seem like a very long time) to allow the blood to clot.

2 If there is any object in the wound, such as a piece of glass, *do not* try to remove it. Simply apply pressure to the sides of the wound.
3 Lay the casualty down and raise the affected part if possible.
4 Make the person comfortable and secure.
5 Dial 999 for an ambulance.

Protect yourself

You should take steps to protect yourself when you are dealing with casualties who are bleeding. Your skin provides an excellent barrier to infections, but you must take care if you have any broken skin such as a cut, graze or sore. Seek medical advice if blood comes into contact with your mouth, nose or gets into your eyes. Blood-borne viruses (such as HIV or hepatitis) can be passed only if the blood of someone who is already infected comes into contact with broken skin.

▶ If possible, wear disposable gloves.
▶ If possible, wash your hands thoroughly in soap and water before and after treatment.
▶ If this is not possible, cover any areas of broken skin with a waterproof dressing.
▶ Take care with any needles or broken glass in the area.
▶ Use a mask for mouth-to-mouth resuscitation if the casualty's nose or mouth is bleeding.

Cardiac arrest

Cardiac arrest occurs when a person's heart stops. Cardiac arrest can happen for various reasons, the most common of which is a heart attack, but a person's heart can also stop as a result of shock, electric shock, a convulsion or other illness or injury.

Symptoms

▶ No pulse
▶ No breathing

Aims

▶ To obtain medical help as a matter of urgency
▶ It is important to give oxygen, using mouth-to-mouth resuscitation, and to stimulate the heart, using chest compressions. This procedure is called cardio-pulmonary resuscitation – CPR. You will need to attend a first aid course to learn how to resuscitate – you cannot learn how to do this from a book. On the first aid course you will be able to practise on a special dummy.

Action

1 Check whether the person has a pulse and whether he or she is breathing.
2 If not, call for urgent help from the emergency services.
3 Start methods of resuscitation *if* you have been taught how to do it.
4 Keep up resuscitation until help arrives.

(a)   (b)

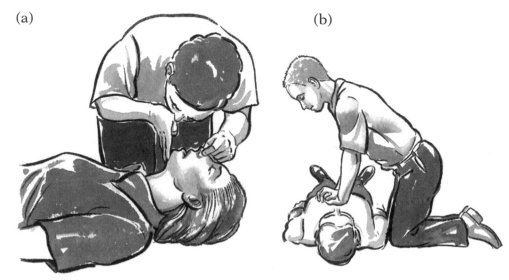

Mouth-to-mouth resuscitation (a) and chest compressions (b).

Shock

Shock occurs because blood is not being pumped around the body efficiently. This can be the result of loss of body fluids through bleeding, burns, severe vomiting or diarrhoea, or a sudden drop in blood pressure or a heart attack.

Symptoms

The signs of shock are easily recognised. The person:

▶ will look very pale, almost grey
▶ will be very sweaty, and the skin will be cold and clammy
▶ will have a very fast pulse
▶ may feel sick and may vomit
▶ may be breathing very quickly.

Aims

▶ To obtain medical help as a matter of urgency
▶ To improve blood supply to heart, lungs and brain

Action

1 Call for urgent medical assistance.
2 Lay the person down on the floor. Try to raise the feet off the ground to help the blood supply to the important organs.

Raise the feet off the ground and keep the casualty warm.

3   Loosen any tight clothing.
4   Watch the person carefully. Check the pulse and breathing regularly.
5   Keep the person warm and comfortable, but *do not* warm the casualty with direct heat, such as a hot water bottle.

Do not:

▶   allow the casualty to eat or drink
▶   leave the casualty alone, unless it is essential to do so briefly in order to summon help.

Loss of consciousness

Loss of consciousness can happen for many reasons, from a straightforward faint to unconsciousness following a serious injury or illness.

Symptom

A reduced level of response and awareness. This can range from being vague and 'woozy' to total unconsciousness.

Aims

▶   To summon expert medical help as a matter of urgency
▶   To keep the airway open
▶   To note any information which may help to establish the cause of the unconsciousness

Action

1   Make sure that the person is breathing and has a clear airway.
2   Maintain the airway by lifting the chin and tilting the head backwards.

Open the airway.

3   Look for any obvious reasons why the person may be unconscious, such as a wound or an ID band telling you of any condition he or she has. For example, many people who have medical conditions which may cause unconsciousness, such as epilepsy or diabetes, will wear special bracelets or necklaces giving information about their condition.
4   Place the casualty in the recovery position (see the next page), *but not if you suspect a back or neck injury*, until the emergency services arrive.

Do not:

▶ attempt to give anything by mouth
▶ attempt to make the casualty sit or stand
▶ leave the casualty alone, unless it is essential to leave briefly in order to summon help.

The recovery position

Many of the actions you need to take to deal with health emergencies will involve you in placing someone in the recovery position. In this position a casualty has the best chance of keeping a clear airway, not inhaling vomit and remaining as safe as possible until help arrives. This position should *not* be attempted if you think someone has back or neck injuries, and it may not be possible if there are fractures of limbs.

(a)

(b)

(c)

The recovery position.

1 Kneel at one side of the casualty, at about waist level.
2 Tilt back the person's head – this opens the airway. With the casualty on his or her back, make sure that limbs are straight.
3 Bend the casualty's near arm as if waving (so it is at right angles to the body). Pull the arm on the far side over the chest and place the back of the hand against the opposite cheek (**a** in diagram opposite).
4 Use your other hand to roll the casualty towards you by pulling on the far leg, just above the knee (**b** in the diagram). The casualty should now be on his or her side.
5 Once the casualty is rolled over, bend the leg at right angles to the body. Make sure the head is tilted well back to keep the airway open (**c** in diagram).

Epileptic seizure

Epilepsy is a medical condition that causes disturbances in the brain which result in sufferers becoming unconscious and having involuntary contractions of their muscles. This contraction of the muscles produces the fit or seizure. People who suffer with epilepsy do not have any control over their seizures, and may do themselves harm by falling when they have a seizure.

Aims

▶ To ensure that the person is safe and does not injure himself or herself during the fit
▶ To offer any help needed following the fit

Action

1 Try to make sure that the area in which the person has fallen is safe.
2 Loosen all clothing.
3 Make sure that the person is comfortable and safe. Particularly try to prevent head injury.
4 Once the seizure has ended, make sure that the person has a clear airway and place in the recovery position.
5 If the fit lasts longer than five minutes, or you are unaware that the casualty is a known epileptic, call an ambulance.

Do not:

▶ attempt to hold the casualty down, or put anything in the mouth
▶ move the casualty until he or she is fully conscious, unless there is a risk of injury in the place where he or she has fallen.

Choking and difficulty with breathing (in adults and children over 8 years)

This is caused by something (usually a piece of food) stuck at the back of the throat. It is a situation which needs to be dealt with, as people can quickly stop breathing if the obstruction is not removed.

Symptoms

▶ Red, congested face at first, later turning grey
▶ Unable to speak or breathe, may gasp and indicate throat or neck

Aims

▶ To remove obstruction as quickly as possible
▶ To summon medical assistance as a matter of urgency if the obstruction cannot be removed

Action

1 Try to get the person to cough. If that is not immediately effective, move on to step 2.
2 Bend the person forwards. Slap sharply on the back between the shoulder blades up to five times (**a** in the diagram on the next page).

3 If this fails, stand behind the person with your arms around him or her. Join your hands just below the breastbone. One hand should be in a fist and the other holding it (**b** in the diagram).

4 Sharply pull your joined hands upwards and into the person's body at the same time. The force should expel the obstruction.

5 You should alternate backslaps and abdominal thrusts until you clear the obstruction.

(a)

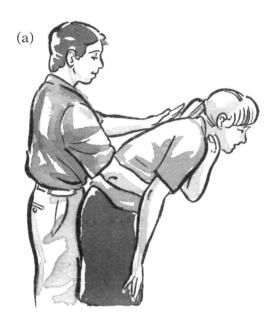

(b)

Dealing with an adult who is choking.

Fractures and suspected fractures

Fractures are breaks or cracks in bones. They are usually caused by a fall or other type of injury. The casualty will need to go to a hospital as soon as possible to have a fracture diagnosed correctly.

Symptoms

▶ Acute pain around the site of the injury
▶ Swelling and discoloration around the affected area
▶ Limbs or joints may be in odd positions
▶ Broken bones may protrude through the skin

Action

1 The important thing is to support the affected part. Help the casualty to find the most comfortable position.

Support the injured limb.

2 Support the injured limb in that position with as much padding as necessary – towels, cushions or clothing will do.

3 Take the person to hospital or call an ambulance.

Do not:

▸ try to bandage or splint the injury

▸ allow the casualty to have anything to eat or drink.

Burns and scalds

There are several different types of burn; the most usual are burns caused by heat or flame. Scalds are caused by hot liquids. People can be burned by chemicals or by electrical currents.

Symptoms

▸ Depending on the type and severity of the burn, skin may be red, swollen and tender, blistered and raw or charred

▸ Usually severe pain and possibly shock

Aims

▸ To obtain immediate medical assistance if the burn is over a large area (as big as the casualty's hand or more) or is deep

▸ To send for an ambulance if the burn is severe or extensive. If the burn or scald is over a smaller area, the casualty could be transported to hospital by car

▸ To stop the burning and reduce pain

▸ To minimise possibility of infection

Action

1 For major burns, summon immediate medical assistance.

2 Cool down the burn. Keep it flooded with cold water for 10 minutes. If it is a chemical burn, this needs to be done for 20 minutes. Ensure that the contaminated water used to cool a chemical burn is disposed of safely.

3 Remove any jewellery, watches or clothing which are not sticking to the burn.

4 Cover the burn if possible, unless it is a facial burn, with a sterile or, at least, clean dressing. For a burn on a hand or foot, a clean plastic bag will protect it from infection until it can be treated by an expert.

Cool the burn with water.

If clothing is on fire, remember the basics: *stop*, *drop*, *wrap* and *roll* the person on the ground.

Do not:

▶ remove anything which is stuck to a burn
▶ touch a burn, or use any ointment or cream
▶ cover facial burns – keep pouring water on until help arrives.

REMEMBER

If a person's clothing is on fire, stop – drop – wrap – roll:

▶ *Stop* him or her from running around.
▶ *Get* him/her to *drop* to the ground – push him/her if you have to and can do so safely.
▶ *Wrap* him/her in something to smother the flames – a blanket or coat, anything to hand. This is better if it is soaked in water
▶ *Roll* him/her on the ground to put out the flames.

Poisoning

People can be poisoned by many substances, drugs, plants, chemicals, fumes or alcohol.

Symptoms

Symptoms will vary depending on the poison.

▶ The person could be unconscious
▶ There may be acute abdominal pain
▶ There may be blistering of the mouth and lips.

Aims

▶ To remove the casualty to a safe area if he/she is at risk, and it is safe for you to move him/her
▶ To summon medical assistance as a matter of urgency
▶ To gather any information which will identify the poison
▶ To maintain a clear airway and breathing until help arrives

Action

1 If the casualty is unconscious, place him/her in the recovery position to ensure that the airway is clear, and that he/she cannot choke on any vomit.
2 Dial 999 for an ambulance.

3 Try to establish what the poison is and how much has been taken. This information could be vital in saving a life.

4 If a conscious casualty has burned mouth or lips, he or she can be given small frequent sips of water or cold milk.

Do not try to make the casualty vomit.

Electrical injuries

Electrocution occurs when an electrical current passes though the body.

Symptoms

Electrocution can cause cardiac arrest and burns where the electrical current entered and left the body.

Aims

▶ To remove the casualty from the current when you can safely do so
▶ To obtain medical assistance as a matter of urgency
▶ To maintain a clear airway and breathing until help arrives
▶ To treat any burns

Action

There are different procedures to follow depending on whether the injury has been caused by a high or low voltage current.

Injury caused by high voltage current

This type of injury may be caused by overhead power cables or rail lines, for example.

1 Contact the emergency services immediately.
2 *Do not* touch the person until all electricity has been cut off.
3 If the person is unconscious, clear the airway.
4 Treat any other injuries present, such as burns.
5 Place in the recovery position until help arrives.

Injury caused by low voltage current

This type of injury may be caused by powered kettles, computers, drills, lawnmowers, etc.

1 Break the contact with the current by switching off the electricity at the mains if possible.
2 It is vital to break the contact as soon as possible, *but* if you touch a person who is 'live' (still in contact with the current) you too will be injured. If you are unable to switch off the electricity, then you must stand on something dry

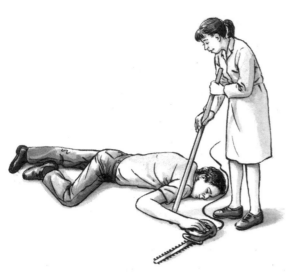

which can insulate you, such as a telephone directory, rubber mat or a pile of newspapers, and then move the casualty away from the current as described below.

3 Do not use anything made of metal, or anything wet, to move the casualty from the current. Try to move him/her with a wooden pole or broom-handle, even a chair.

4 Alternatively, drag him/her with a rope or cord or, as a last resort, pull by holding any of the person's dry clothing which is *not* in contact with his/her body.

5 Once the person is no longer in contact with the current, you should follow the same steps as with a high voltage injury.

Move the casualty away from the current.

Check it out

1 You should always attempt first aid even if you have not been trained, because it is always better to do something. True or false?

2 What is the single most important act for an untrained person to do in a health emergency?

Other ways to help

Summon assistance

In the majority of cases this will mean telephoning 999 and requesting an ambulance. It will depend on the setting in which you work and clearly is not required if you work in a hospital! But it may mean calling for a colleague with medical qualifications, who will then be able to make an assessment of the need for further assistance. Similarly, if you work in the residential sector, there should be a medically qualified colleague available. If you are the first on the scene at an emergency in the community, you may need to summon an ambulance for urgent assistance.

If you need to call an ambulance, try to keep calm and give clearly all the details you are asked for. Do not attempt to give details until they are asked for – this wastes time. Emergency service operators are trained to find out the necessary information, so let them ask the questions, then answer calmly and clearly.

Follow the action steps outlined in the previous section while you are waiting for help to arrive.

Assist the person dealing with the emergency

A second pair of hands is invaluable when dealing with an emergency. If you are assisting someone with first aid or medical expertise, follow all his or her instructions, even if you don't understand why. An emergency situation is not the time for a discussion or debate – that can happen later. You may be needed to help to move a casualty, or to fetch water, blankets or dressings, or to reassure and comfort the casualty during treatment.

Make the area safe

An accident or injury may have occurred in an unsafe area – and it was probably for precisely that reason that the accident occurred there! Sometimes, it may be that the accident has made the area unsafe for others. For example, if someone has tripped over an electric flex, there may be exposed wires or a damaged electric socket. Alternatively, a fall against a window or glass door may have left shards of broken glass in the area, or there may be blood or other body fluids on the floor. You may need to make the area safe by turning off the power, clearing broken glass or dealing with a spillage.

It may be necessary to redirect people away from the area of the accident in order to avoid further casualties.

Maintain the privacy of the casualty

You may need to act to provide some privacy for the casualty by asking onlookers to move away or stand back. If you can erect a temporary screen with coats or blankets, this may help to offer some privacy. It may not matter to the casualty at the time, but he or she has a right to privacy if possible.

Make accurate reports

You may be responsible for making a report on an emergency situation you have witnessed, or for filling in records later. Concentrate on the most important aspects of the incident and record the actions of yourself and others in an accurate, legible and complete manner. See the example of an accident report on page 171.

How to deal with witnesses' distress – and your own

People who have witnessed accidents can often be very distressed by what they have seen. The distress may be as a result of the nature of the injury, or the blood loss. It could be because the casualty is a friend or relative or simply because seeing accidents or injuries is traumatic. Some people can become upset because they feel helpless and do not know how to assist, or they may have been afraid and then feel guilty later.

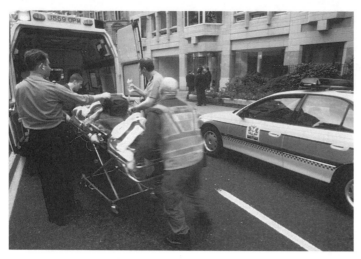
Witnessing accidents is often distressing.

You will need to reassure people about the casualty and the fact that he or she is being cared for appropriately. However, do not give false reassurance about things you may not be sure of.

You may need to allow individuals to talk about what they saw. One of the commonest effects of witnessing a trauma is that people need to repeat over and over again what they saw.

What about you?

You may feel very distressed by the experience you have gone through. You may find that you need to talk about what has happened, and that you need to look again at the role you played. You may feel that you could have done more, or you may feel angry with yourself for not having a greater knowledge about what to do.

There is a whole range of emotions which you may experience. You should be able to discuss your feelings with your supervisor and use any support provided by your employer.

If you have followed the basic guidelines in this outcome, you will have done as much as could be expected of anyone at the scene of an emergency who is not a trained first aider.

Outcome activity 5.2

You could undertake this activity in a group or by yourself. You are to produce an explanatory report, which can be completed as a word-processed document in hard copy or viewed on-line.

Step 1
Read the following scenario:

You are a support worker in the community and are visiting an older service user, Mrs J. She lives alone, but has friends and relatives who also visit. You go twice each week to provide general support services.

When you arrive one day, you are met with the following scene. Mrs J is lying on the floor, looking grey, and is cold and clammy. Her breathing is very shallow and infrequent, and she does not appear to be conscious. Her sister, Mrs P, who was visiting when she was taken ill, tried to help her and fell against the fireplace, badly cutting her leg which is bleeding heavily. She is conscious, but in a lot of pain. An elderly neighbour, Mrs N, heard the crash and commotion and is also there. She does not appear to be hurt, but is very pale and trembling.

Step 2
Explain what actions you would take, and in what order. Use bullet points, or a numbered list, or a table. Make sure that you explain why you would take each of the actions listed, and give reasons for the order in which you would do them.

Glossary

Advocacy   The process of speaking or acting to protect an individual's rights.

Assessment tools   Formal methods of collecting information to enable an assessment to be made.

Awareness agencies   Agencies supplying information about specific issues or conditions.

Care plan   The outline of an individual's present and future needs and how these are to be met.

Care standards   Defined standards of good practice which can be measured and evaluated.

Care team   Those people who have a responsibility for the care of an individual including the person himself or herself.

Care work   The process of supporting people with their personal needs.

Challenging behaviour   Behaviour that is demanding and/or disruptive and which results in difficulties in providing quality care.

Client   The individual who is receiving care, e.g. service users, residents in residential care, patients in acute settings.

Client-centred approach   The client's needs determine the plan of care rather than the services that are available.

COSHH   Control of Substances Hazardous to Health.

ESOL   English for speakers of other languages.

Experiential learning   Learning from experience.

Holistic   Consideration of the person as a whole, not just seeing each part/problem in isolation.

Management of continence   The means by which individuals can be helped to achieve continence or the practical measures to help them cope with incontinence.

Medipak   A labelled container with instructions for clear use of day and time of intake.

Multi-disciplinary approach   Different disciplines having an understanding of each other's roles and responsibilities in respect of an individual's care.

Multi-disciplinary team   People from different disciplines who work together and have responsibility for a person's care.

Multi-disciplinary work   The process of working with other disciplines to provide care for an individual.

National Occupational Standards Standards set and agreed nationally by employers and other interested parties as to what constitutes best practice in particular occupational areas.

Norton pressure system A system for assessing the individual's susceptibility to develop pressure sores.

Personal profile Details of an individual's life, background and experience which enables others to see him or her as a whole person.

PISCES/SPICES Physical, Intellectual, Social, Cultural, Emotional, Spiritual needs, Sexual needs.

Preventative Actions which are designed to stop something undesirable from happening.

Quality standards Standards set locally which are used to gauge the quality of the service provided.

Reflective learning The consideration of action so that skills, knowledge, values and emotional response can be developed.

Reflective practitioner A worker who considers his or her actions so that skills, knowledge, values and emotional response can be developed.

Remedial Putting actions into place which will counteract or remove anything unwanted.

RIDDOR Reporting of Injuries, Diseases and Dangerous Occurrences Regulations.

SMART Specific, Measurable, Achievable, Realistic, Targeted/Timed, normally related to objectives.

Target groups The people for whom a specific service is intended.

Therapeutic A structured programme of activities designed specifically to effect some change in an individual's behaviour or condition.

Transactions The way that individuals conduct their relationships.

Key skills

	Communication	Application of number	IT	Improving own learning and performance	Problem solving	Working with others
Outcome Activity 1.1 (page 26)	✓		✓		✓	✓
Outcome Activity 1.2 (page 42)	✓		✓		✓	✓
Outcome Activity 1.3 (page 52)	✓		✓	✓	✓	✓
Outcome Activity 1.4 (page 80)	✓		✓			
Outcome Activity 1.5 (page 91)	✓		✓		✓	✓
Outcome Activity 2.1 (page 113)	✓			✓		✓
Outcome Activity 2.2 (page 119)	✓		✓	✓		✓
Outcome Activity 2.3 (page 135)	✓		✓			
Outcome Activity 3.1 (page 142)	✓		✓	✓		
Outcome Activity 3.2 (page 151)	✓		✓	✓		✓
Outcome Activity 3.3 (page 164)	✓		✓		✓	✓
Outcome Activity 5.1 (page 178)	✓	✓	✓			
Outcome Activity 5.2 (page 192)	✓		✓		✓	

Index

Headings in *italics* refer to publications; page number in *italics* to illustrations.

practice 138
secrecy, and abuse disclosures 70–1
security
    of computer records 99–101
    of e-mails 103–4
    of faxes 93–4, 103
    of houses 176
    and intruders 98, 174–5
    of personal property 176–7
    and the telephone 98, 102, 103
    of vulnerable adults 175
self-concept 30
self-confidence 28–9
self-esteem 28
self-harm 58
self-neglect 60–2
service users
    addressing 30
    communication with 41–2, *41*, *42*
    and complaints 24
    consultation with 33, 34
    cultural values of 30–1
    formal support of 23
    informal support of 23–4
    religious beliefs of 30–1
    restricting access to 177
    and rights support 21–4, *22*, 25
    unacceptable behaviour by 82–3
    valuing 32, 33–4, 42
severe bleeding 180–1, *180*
Sex Discrimination Act 1975 8–10
sexist abuse 58
sexual abuse
    definitions of 57
    signs and symptoms of 65–6
shock 182–3, *183*
    electric 189–90, *190*
    about abuse 74
social needs 37, 38
standards, national 52
stereotyping 12–14, 133
stress
    causes of 157–8
    dealing with 158–9, *159*
    results of 157
    support for 159–60
strokes 121, 129
supervision 140–1
supervisors 145
support
    and stress 159–60
    teamwork 141, 160–1

teamwork
    and conflict resolution 21, 161–2
    and decision making 20
    developing 20–1
    and informal support 141, 160–1
    and motivation 163
telephone
    caller identity 98, 103
    security of 98, 102, 103
    use of 93
training
    see also learning; professional
        development
    for physical restraint 90
    utilising 157

unacceptable behaviour
    see also violent behaviour
    causes of 82, 85
    colleagues' 81–2
    dealing with 83
    definitions of 81
    examples of 81, 162
unconsciousness 183–4, *183*, *184*
United Nations Declaration on
    Human Rights 1–2

values, exploring own 44–6
Valuing People 77, 79
violent behaviour
    see also aggression
    calming 83–4
    dealing with 84–5
visits, and health and safety 177–8
visual impairment, and
    communication 121, 128, 132
vulnerable adults
    abuse of *57*, *64*, 67
    definitions of 57
    protection of 78–9, 175

whistle-blowing 72
women
    equal opportunities for 8–10
    equal pay for 8
*Working Together to Safeguard
    Children* 76–7

Your Guide to the NHS 3, 18

S 666 CAR A

The best-selling title for the Level 3 award

S/NVQ Level 3 Care

This popular title offers a complete and concise learning package for the NVQ and SVQ in Care. The easy-to-read text covers the five mandatory units at Level 3 and all 13 Group A option units, giving you enough material to achieve a full award. S/NVQ Level 3 Care includes:

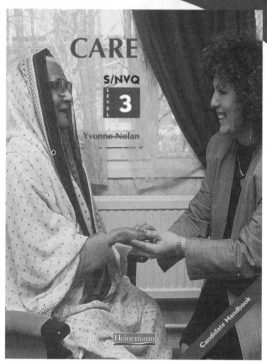

◆ Case Studies to encourage you to apply your learning to scenarios in the workplace;

◆ Test Yourself sections to ensure you understand all the theory you have learnt;

0 435 45642 3

◆ Active Knowledge tasks to help you apply the theory in your workplace.

Why not order a copy of S/NVQ Level 3 Care today?

Visit your local bookshop or contact our Customer Services Department for more details:

ⓣ 01865 888068 ⓕ 01865 314029 ⓔ orders@heinemann.co.uk ⓦ www.heinemann.co.uk

Heinemann
Inspiring generations